Healing Soil

Endorsements for 'Healing Soil'

“All who are concerned with the future of the planet will find Bruce Ball's ideas and vision in this book well worth working towards. He clearly explains good soil health and how this is important for sustainable agriculture and for helping tackle climate change and pollution. He takes us beyond the direct effects of soil health by drawing spiritual parallels between soils and humanity, culminating in a remarkable vision of a world inspired by soil. This intellectual masterpiece, pertinent to addressing global issues of the 21st century by restoring soil health, is of interest to soil scientists, general public, religious organisations, and, of course, the policymakers. I strongly support the book because its ideas will remain useful for generations to come.”

Professor Rattan Lal, *Distinguished Professor of Soil Science and Director Rattan Lal Centre for Carbon Management and Sequestration*, The Ohio State University, USA.

“Bruce Ball's book is an informed reflection on the role of soils in underpinning civilization and the continued sustainability of our planet and our species. He is a respected retired soil scientist with over 35 years of professional experience to draw upon, and many more years of curiosity and interest in soils before that. As a spiritual man, he also brings a unique perspective, that goes well beyond the science. As well as crafting the text, he illustrates the book with his own poetry, art work and photographs. This labour of love will inform and enchant its readers, be they knowledgeable environmental scientists, or people learning about soils for the first time.”

Professor Pete Smith, FRS, FRSE, FNA, FEurAsc, FRSB *Distinguished Professor of Soils and Global Change*, University of Aberdeen, Scotland, UK.

“Bruce Ball needs to be heard by everyone concerned about the way we are living today. He is a passionate and dedicated scientist with a lifetime's experience of working with and teaching about the soil. But he also has an amazing ability to bring out the spiritual dimensions and benefits of engaging with the soil and of using it to urgently *reconnect soul with soil* in a way that will empower the non-specialist to get their hands dirty and change their life for the better.

This is a real gem of a book that is engagingly written and stunningly illustrated with his own art and poetry, this book offers insights into the need to explore and cherish the staggering diversity of life under the soil that will inform, delight, and challenge everyone. A must-buy gift for anyone with a heart for the planet!”

Revd Dr Terry Biddington, FRSA, FLS, *Dean of Spiritual Life, Director of the Winchester Institute for Contemplative Education*, University of Winchester, UK and Scholar of Ecology.

Healing Soil

How soil health will save the planet and us

Bruce C Ball

2022

First published in 2022 by Bruce Ball, Roslin, Midlothian, UK

ISBN: 978-1-7395931-0-0 (Paperback)
ISBN: 978-1-7395931-1-7 (eBook)

Printed and distributed by Kindle Direct Publishing Services, Amazon, Seattle, Washington, USA
Typeset by Pageset Ltd, High Wycombe, Buckinghamshire HP11 1JR

Front cover: 'Broken Earth' *Oil on board.*

CONTENTS

FOREWORD

The Foreword is by **Dr Cat Ball**, the author's daughter:

As the daughter of a committed soil scientist, an awareness of the importance of the soil has been a constant in my life. I have fond childhood memories of going for hill walks with my Dad where he'd animatedly point out the quality of the soil, its structure or some other aspect he found interesting (which, needless to say, I often didn't find as fascinating as he did…). Sadly he was often pointing out damage that had been done as a result of erosion or other man-made processes. He spoke about climate change, peak oil, no-tillage and soil degradation well before they became popular buzz words. And he often went on trips to far-flung locations to measure greenhouse gases from the soil or to develop methods of measuring soil structure.

In my teenage years I fit the type and grew a bit disinterested in my Dad's wisdom. However, when I went to university, and I was exposed to the world of environmental activism, I realised that my Dad was more enlightened than most and a bit of a trailblazer. Around this time he began talking about the spiritual parallels between soil and humanity, and how society could benefit from learning lessons from the soil. I probably thought he was a bit barmy at this point but I knew he had a voice that should be heard so I encouraged him to write his first book – The Landscape Below.

I now work in science and research policy. When I first started out I got a bit too much into a focus on scientific evidence and found myself turning away from spirituality to 'hard facts'. As I've got older though I've once more found myself coming back around to my Dad's way of thinking and the realisation that, again, he's ahead of his time. It's been amazing to watch him spread his message to the many people who've read his book and listened to the talks and presentations he's given. And since his retirement he's found a new medium to communicate – his art and his creative interpretations of the soil and the environment (which are a lot better than his portraits of my mother, trust me).

This book has been a long time coming. It has evolved through many conversations and interactions with students, farmers, scientists, friends, Church groups and, ultimately, my Dad's experiences growing up and the deep connection with the soil that it fostered in him. I hope that this book allows you to get to know soil a little better while also revealing some insights about us as people too. Soil is not just something that gets stuck to your boots; it plays a crucial role in providing us with food and fresh water, and it can show us the road to a more sustainable life.

Dr Cat Ball currently works in Research and Innovation Policy in Edinburgh.

ABOUT THIS BOOK

This book is a journey that explores the importance of our soil to our world and humanity and the connection that can be found between soil and both of these. Each of the three parts contains a series of short illustrated items spotlighting a key way that soil contributes to the health of ourselves, our society and our planet. The items are illustrated either by artworks that I have created or by photographs to show the interplay between the fate of the soil and the fate of our world – from all of humanity down to the way we live our individual lives. The health of the planet is a central theme so each artwork is modelled on the globe of the Earth or contains at least its outline. Most items relate to my experiences of working with soil throughout my 35-year career in soil science and farming and discovering more and more how important soil is to our lives.

Soil is under major threat due to erosion and poor land use – 40 % of African soils are degraded with poverty driving many farmers to overgrazing or omitting to return fertility after cropping. Extremes of heat and drought are bringing desertification to agricultural land in Europe, sub-Saharan Africa and America's west. Soil health is dwindling in every corner of our planet.

Images in the book show what soil health is and how it can be improved by sustainable soil management that also increases crop food quality and stores carbon from the atmosphere. Pictures also illustrate soil properties that are shown to parallel human traits and behaviour. Identifying and learning from these parallels can help us to bring mental and physical healing and a mind to improve our world. This culminates in an image of a soil-based world that expresses how drawing parallels of our behaviour with soil properties can help to tackle hunger, bring healing and hints for tackling problems in society.

A new sense of urgency to address environmental and human health has been created by the Covid-19 pandemic. A wake-up call to action has been sounded at all levels from our families to the global community – we need to realise our connectivity to Nature and to others throughout the world.

The book is arranged in three parts that focus on achieving healthy soil, a healthy planet and healthy lives. At the end of the book there are sections where you are invited to take part in activities to get to know your local soil better and to take a spiritual journey inspired by soil to help reflect on the ideas presented here, gaining fresh perspectives that may help secure the future health of the planet and of all of the life that depends upon it. Many of my messages came through contacts with students, farmers, scientists and community workers. I have given some of these their voice to add personal interest. All artworks, photographs and poetry are by the author unless stated otherwise.

Broken Earth

Oil on board. The Earth was modelled by a tennis ball.

We are breaking the body of our hospitable globe and losing our grip on soil, fresh water and greenhouse gases. Much of the soil and the nutrients within it are washed into the sea. Without topsoil the earth's ability to feed people, absorb carbon and filter and store water almost disappears.

Part I. Healthy Soil

Healthy soil is vital for the production of crops for our food, it's the home to much of our planet's biodiversity, it stores and purifies water and, what's more, it helps to lock-up carbon to slow climate change. These functions depend on maintaining good proportions of air and water in soil and on conserving the life in the soil. When soil loses its health, it becomes degraded and can be readily lost by being carried off by wind or water.

In this part, I describe soil and its properties with emphasis on its layers, porosity and the life within. I reveal the main differences between healthy soil and degraded soil. I show the importance of porosity, the diversity of soil life and how the interconnected networks of porosity and of soil life are important for soils to function properly. I then begin to draw parallels between these connections and properties with the functions of our planet, the workings of our mind, co-operation and community building. These aspects help us to understand the healing of mind and body. I then describe a simple method of assessing soil health that I developed with colleagues. Finally, I introduce how we depend on healthy soil for producing healthy food.

All life has its roots in soil

Acrylic on paper.

Roots draw moisture and nutrients from the soil to nourish the plant to bring us food, fibre or flower. The beauty of a flower and of a person are rooted together in the soil and, ultimately, all living Nature is nourished by these roots. Whether we know it or not, we are all connected to the soil and depend on it to nurture us physically and mentally whether by bringing beauty such as flowers, nutrient-rich food from crops or calmness of mind and spirit by walking along paths or working in our gardens.

> “*Whether we know it or not we are all connected to the soil*”

The layers of soil

Acrylic on board. The textures were created using plastic beads and fragments bonded with glue. This shows a slice of soil taken from the surface to approximately 1.2 m depth. It is a Kauri podsol from Northland in New Zealand and is based on a photograph[1].

Pale below, colour above
A hard thin layer between
Podsolization *Paul Hargreaves*

Soil forms from a parent material of rock or sediment that is slowly eroded by water into small particles in which plants and microorganisms grow to eventually create a layer of soil. The process continues for many years to build up a soil. The soil develops layers of different colours called horizons; at least six distinct horizons are shown, though, in many soils, three horizons are more common. The soil is made dark by the organic material accumulated from decomposed plant and microbial material. The dark layer near the surface is the topsoil and is where most carbon from the atmosphere is stored within decomposed plant material.

There are many different types of soils. Podsols are a typical soil type in temperate zones. They are highly acidic and usually have a bleached horizon (shown in blue here) below the topsoil. The dark zone below the pale horizon contains mineral nutrients and organic matter washed down by rainwater from the horizons above. The bleached horizon and the layer below are called the subsoil. The lighter coloured layers of sandstone below are called the parent material, the basic foundation of rock or deposit from which the soil is formed. The parent material has a fundamental influence on the chemistry, the colour and the feel of soil.

Healthy soil and degraded soil

Photographs are of loamy soil in East Lothian, courtesy of Rachel Guimarães. Illustrations are watercolour and felt tip pen on paper.

Healthy soil is made up of porous soil lumps called aggregates. The diagrams below each photograph show cross sections that reveal that aggregates are actually made up of smaller aggregates of a range of sizes (shown in red). These smaller aggregates in turn are made up of solid particles of sand surrounded by smaller silt and clay particles. The proportions of these different types of particles are summarised in the term soil texture and remain the same at a given location. The space between aggregates or solid particles is the soil porosity. The more spaces the more porous the soil. A healthy soil is about half solid particles and half (50%) porosity. Typically, about half of the porosity is filled with water (in blue) and half contains soil air (in green). The water surrounds the aggregates and fills the small spaces between them. Thus the porosity allows water to be stored for plant growth. The larger spaces that are air-filled provide oxygen and living spaces for soil life. The air-filled spaces also store rainwater that percolates into the soil. Roots (in yellow) also grow through the porosity. Unlike texture, porosity varies with the health of the soil. The sizes and porosities of the aggregates that make up the soil is called the soil structure. The quality of the soil structure is an indicator of soil health also known as soil quality.

Soil becomes unhealthy soil when it is subjected to excessive external forces, like those from water or machinery. Unhealthy soil can also result from the addition of pollutants. Soil that is unhealthy is called degraded. External forces squeeze and deform the aggregates, reducing the porosity and the important connections between pores. This makes it harder for roots to grow and restricts the supply of oxygen to the soil life. It also reduces the ability of the soil to store water and increases the chance of rainfall running off the soil surface.

Some years ago, I had a field experiment comparing tillage methods on a sloping site near Edinburgh. Before the experiment began, the soil near the surface was mostly degraded, carrying crop residues and weeds. I remember walking through it just after a heavy shower of rain. In the stillness, I could just hear the water trickling across the surface and see some of the stalks of the crop residues vibrating as the water passed. Fertiliser or pesticide residues at the surface would have been carried off in the water to the stream at the bottom of the slope.

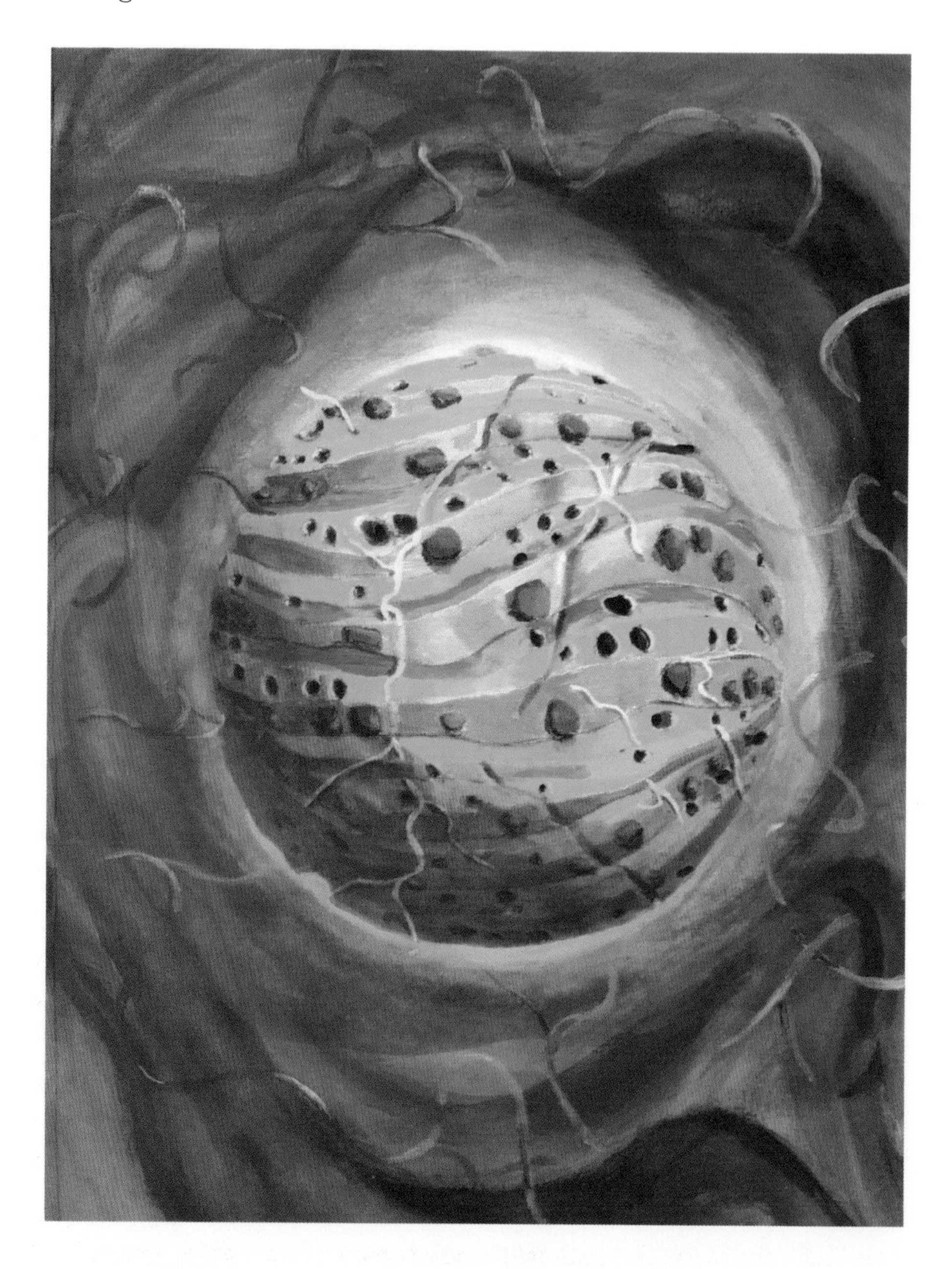

A healthy soil aggregate and the importance of porosity

The aggregate was modelled using a small football that was covered in strips of paper to roughly represent the proportion of soil that is solid and the proportion of soil that is space between the solids, the porosity. Dot stickers were attached to the ball to represent large pores and sand particles. This was photographed to give a guide to perspective during painting.

The red represents the proportion of mineral particles with the red dots representing the sand particles standing out. As in the image of 'Healthy soil and Degraded soil', the green represents the proportion of porosity filled with air and the blue represents the porosity filled with water. The large pores are shown as holes and as channels crossing the surface of the porosity (blue and green bands). Roots are shown in white. Roots are also shown more magnified in the surrounds as thick rope-like structures enmeshed in coils of fungal filaments. These filaments are tubular strings like the branches of a tree. The aggregate is held together by the roots, the fungal filaments and organic glues – a microcosm of our Earth.

Soil life – and all life – depends on soil porosity. A satisfactory amount of porosity that is well-connected is vital for the soil to function well. Without healthy soil, plant growth, agriculture, water supply and carbon storage in plants and soils would be impossible and oil and coal would never have been created.

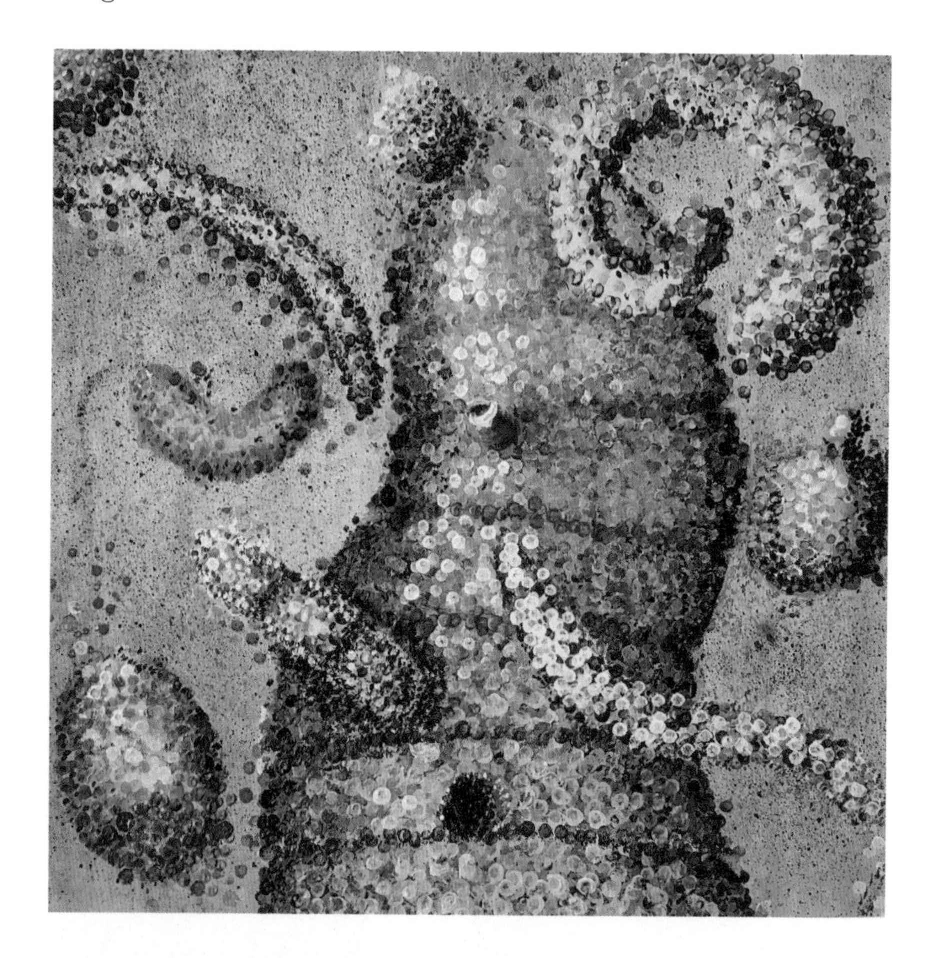

The Dazzling Array of Soil Life

Acrylic on paper. Pointillism, where paint is applied in dots and small discs, was used to show the continuum of size of soil organisms from microscopic (around 0.002 mm to clearly visible around 2 mm). The small background dots represent bacteria and the large central portion is the tip of an earthworm.

Soil contains an incredible variety of living organisms of a vast range of sizes all living off each other and on the plant material accumulated in the soil – this makes up the soil food web[2]. Organisms include bacteria, fungi, algae, nematodes, grubs, mites, beetles and earthworms. When all of this myriad of interconnecting organisms is present and functioning, growth and decay are in balance and soil biodiversity is good. This makes the soil healthy and brings benefits to human health[3]. I'll talk about this in greater detail later in the book.

Incredibly, the soil aggregates shown on page 6 contain more living organisms than there are people on the Earth. When combined with living and decomposing plant material, living organisms form the organic matter in soil. Typically, only about 5% of soil is organic matter. Thus, even a small loss of this vital component of the soil reduces our soil's health, making it vulnerable to degradation by wind, water, animals and machinery and making it less effective at supporting growth and sustaining life. Soil supports plant growth by supplying water, nutrients and an interconnected network of porosity for root and shoot development.

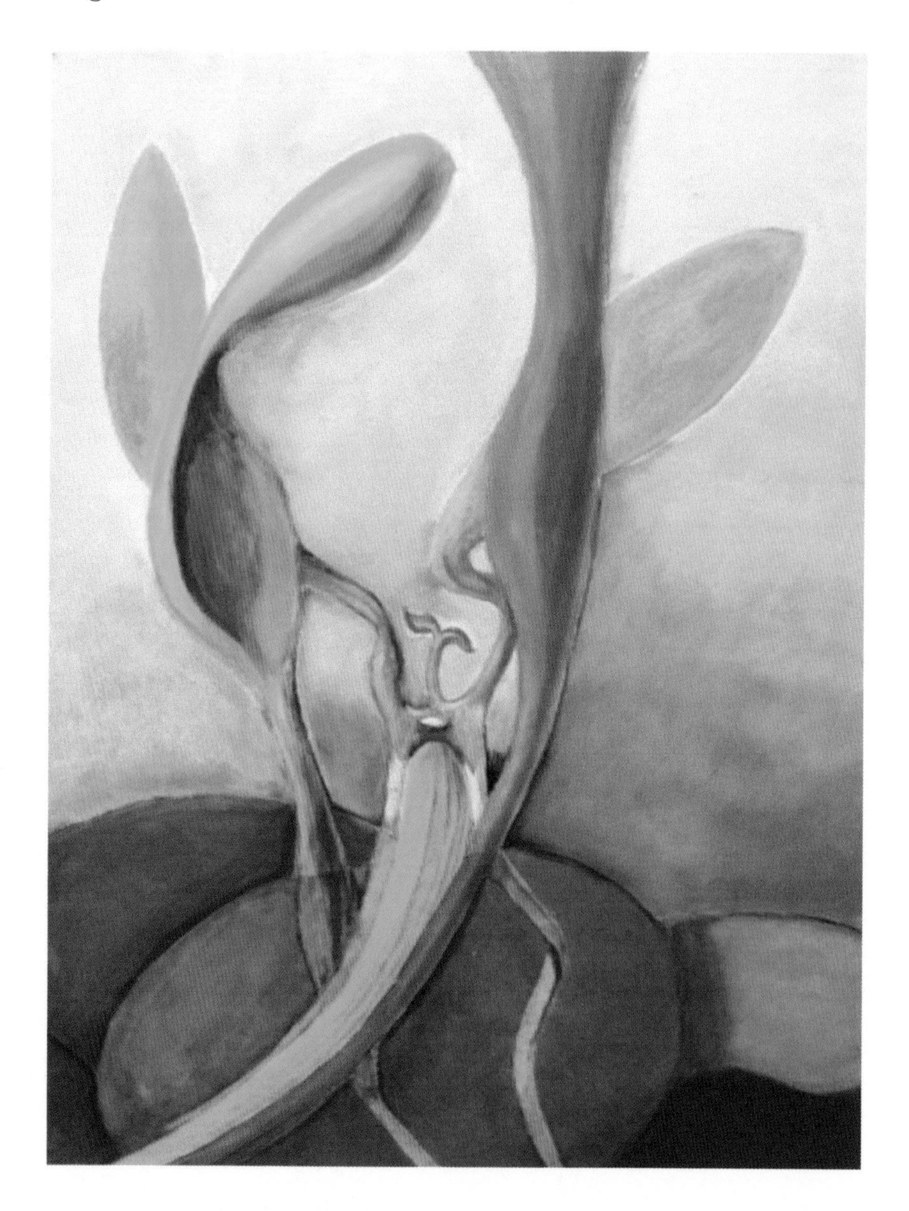

Soil Greening Power: Connecting the scientific and the spiritual

Acrylic on board.

'Fall soft where you belong, my seed
I need you
The future depends on me' *Naima Penniman*

The seed, sown in hope and shown at the centre, is urged to life by the 'greening power' from the soil, represented by the curved green cylinder thrusting towards the seed.

Greening power – the ability to grow something green – is an emotional image of the creative energy of the soil. It was a name given by the first soil scientist to write about the soil, the nun Hildegaard von Bingen, for the energy which infuses seeds with life. This turns the surface of a recently sown field from brown to a light, velvet green as the seedlings germinate and emerge from the soil.

> *"Greening power – the ability to grow something green – is an emotional image of the creative energy of the soil"*

Greening power is an image of the spirit in the soil. This power is a link between the science of the study of crop growth (agronomy) and the spiritual. Greening power also includes ideas of vitality, vigour and freshness. Hildegaard von Bingen considered it to come from God and that it was in everything, interconnecting us to the natural world, including the soil, and to the Divine. This link extends to healing. In her book on 'Slow Healing', the physician Victoria Sweet[4] considers that von Bingen believed that human healing resembles the soil's greening power and regenerating capabilities of plant life. Sweet also proposes that healing should include the idea of gardening in the body, nourishing greening power and removing that which gets in its way.

As well as the first soil scientist, Hildegard von Bingen was a theologian, a music composer and an artist, producing mainly religious images[5]. Perhaps her art influenced her thinking in classifying soils in terms of colour. Her interest in soil was remarkable because she combined ideas of science with expressions of art and spirituality. In this way, science can move from reductionism to holism – the belief that systems should be viewed as wholes rather than collections of parts. A good example is our Earth which can be viewed as a system that works together so that the overall effect is greater than the sum of the parts – the concept of Gaia[6]. Gaia is the idea that the components of the Earth function as a single system, regarded as an organism, such that living components maintain conditions suitable for life.

Both spirituality and art involve engaging the emotions and can help enable the understanding of complex scientific ideas. I believe that they also facilitate the creative interpretation of science – for example to help the understanding of human behaviour.

To sustain our soils in the future we need to nurture the good greening power of the soil – almost all (95%) of our food is grown in it.

Resilient soil: humus rich and healthy

This soil is from near the surface in an old natural forest in Bilston Glen, near Edinburgh. The aggregates are loose and porous and the soil biodiversity is good. The decay of dead roots, leaves and soil creatures provides a high content of organic matter to the soil. The oldest and most decomposed organic matter is humus, giving the soil a rich, dark colour and nutty, fresh smell.

Dark, firm and fertile
Rich in humus, sweet of smell
Complex living soil *Paul Hargreaves*

The words 'human', 'humble' and 'humility' are derived from humus. Increasing humility, like increasing the humus and organic matter content of the soil, increases the power of the soil (or a person) to recover from shocks, thus increasing their resilience.

My soil biologist colleague, **Professor Bryan Griffiths**, writes: 'soil resilience depends on the stability of the soil microbial community and is related to the diversity of microbes present and to the microstructure of the soil[7]. The microbes live in the pores within this small-scale structure and on decaying plant material. Soil resilience is measured by experimentally disturbing the soil to reflect either short-lived disturbances or continuous, pressure-type disturbances. A short-lived disturbance, which could be described as 'here today, gone tomorrow', will affect microbial activity in, for example, a drought period or in human terms our ability to carry on as normal in a heatwave. A continuous, chronic type of disturbance is more of a long-term feature and requires adaptation by the organisms affected. Examples are the microbial responses to heavy-metal pollution or to permanent soil compaction, while a human example would be respiratory responses to long-term air pollution.'

The forest where this soil came from is close to my home and is a popular area for walkers. However, houses are being built around it and there is a risk it could be cut down to make way for houses or roads. Then the soil would be scraped up, put into huge mounds and moved around the building sites as it progressively deteriorates. Such a loss.

Soil health: vulnerable to subtle change

This image, taken in the early 1970's, shows my home where I was brought up in Clatt, a small village in North-east Scotland.

This land surrounding Clatt is some of the most productive in the UK, much of it due to a very good soil of medium texture, good drainage and high natural fertility along with a favourable climate. The soil in this image was all ploughed and would soon have been sown to barley, turnips or potatoes. Ploughing is the traditional tillage for the area and is used to prepare the land for sowing crops. In my mind, the soil looks darker than when viewed 50 years later, suggesting a possible progressive loss of humus – but then it could relate to the quality of the original photograph!

The extreme weather associated with climate change in recent years has made many farmers and soil scientists wary of exposing the soil in this way other than for a few days a year, because it is vulnerable to erosion by water or wind.

Soil Depletion and Global Change

Acrylic and plastic beads on canvas. This sideways view of a soil profile is progressively depleted with time (moving from left to right) by a combination of global change and intensive agriculture. Depletion involves the overall thinning of the soil, loss of stored water, increased gaseous emissions of carbon, loss of nutrients and erosion of topsoil to rivers and seas. This picture was first published in a scientific paper.[8]

Almost half of the world's most productive soil has disappeared in the last 150 years. In developed countries this is mainly because of intensive or industrial agriculture. Large areas of crops are often grown continuously year after year, depleting soil organic matter and compacting the soil. In developing countries with few resources, a combination

> *"Almost half of the world's most productive soil has disappeared in the last 150 years"*

of deforestation and overgrazing or cropping without adding organic fertilisers can result in desertification and dramatic soil losses. Soil is lost due to degradation as a result of the reduction in the stability of soil structure, mainly due to the loss of organic matter and a lessening in the binding action of roots. Often this is made worse by removing protective vegetation and residues from the soil surface[9], thereby reducing biodiversity[10]. The soil also needs to be maintained at a near neutral pH – not too acidic and not too alkaline. Loss of topsoil can result in increased soil acidity which means that nutrients are less available and the soil's structure is less stable.

Rapid expansion and unsustainable management of croplands and grasslands are considered to be the most extensive direct global causes of land degradation, resulting in significant losses of biodiversity, food security, water purification and energy[11]. Land degradation is also a major contributor to climate change through deforestation and the release of carbon previously stored in the soil[11].

Degraded land has soil of poor health.

The scars and open sores of soil erosion

Madagascar is the 'great red island' off the East Coast of Africa. The colour results from the orange-red lateritic soil, a consequence of the high levels of iron. Trees have been cut down and the grassland has been overgrazed by local farmers trying to survive. During extreme weather this results in dramatic soil degradation as erosion by rainwater exposes the subsoil. Seen from the air, Madagascar can appear to be bleeding into the ocean. Photograph courtesy of Marinus Brouwers.

Professor Rattan Lal, President of the International Union of Soil Sciences, 2017, stated that **'Humans are an integral part of the soil. Thus, whatever harm we may do to the soil will also happen to us'**.

Woodland soil; loose and healthy

Cereal cropped soil; compact and short of oxygen

Compaction: crushing the soil's lungs

These photographs are of the same soil type separated by less than 100 m. They show the tremendous influence of the way land is managed on soil structure and soil health. The upper image shows a clayey soil under woodland where a very good soil structure with distinct porous aggregates and organic matter and humus are evident. The lower image shows the same soil nearby

> *but sown to winter wheat. Mis-used agricultural machinery has broken and compacted the soil, crushing the aggregates together into a solid lump, breaching and squeezing out the connections of much of the porosity.*

Soil life breathes through the air-filled porosity which contains nitrogen, oxygen and carbon dioxide in roughly the same proportions as in the atmosphere. Compaction makes the soil less effective as a growing medium and the ruined porosity readily fills with rainwater, waterlogging the soil and cutting off much of the oxygen supply to the soil biology and the roots so that carbon dioxide builds up and they become asphyxiated. This makes it difficult for the soil organisms to respire. In these circumstances, oxygen-starved microorganisms turn to iron and manganese oxides as a source of oxygen, reducing them to colourless or grey compounds so that the soil become grey or even blue in colour – a clear sign that the soil is gasping for air – known as poor soil aeration. Nitrogen oxides in solution – often present as synthetic fertilisers – are also reduced to the greenhouse gas nitrous oxide[12]. Another consequence of compaction allowing the rainfall to quickly fill up the restricted porosity is that the excess then runs off, often taking the soil with it, causing erosion.

In waterlogged soil, earthworms usually hide in pockets of trapped air and coil up into balls to survive. During drainage after several days of flooding, the soil organisms and functions usually recover though the greater the initial porosity then the better the recovery of the greening power.

Compacted soil is also hard, especially when it dries, preventing roots from moving freely through it. In the compacted soil above, the roots are growing only in the cracks and through some large pores. Although this soil was degraded, it managed to support a crop because the small root system was nevertheless effective because a combination of the free availability of synthetic fertiliser applied by the farmer and the moist soil allowed ready uptake of water and nutrients by roots. Even when damaged a soil can be moderately productive – but at a cost – mainly to environmental and possibly human health due to the low crop uptake of the applied synthetic nitrogen fertiliser[13] (see page 34).

I have seen compaction extend down to nearly 1 m depth. Such subsoil compaction can be found in some Brazilian soils where sugar cane is harvested by road-going lorries. Very deep compaction cannot be loosened by cultivation and may persist for a long time.

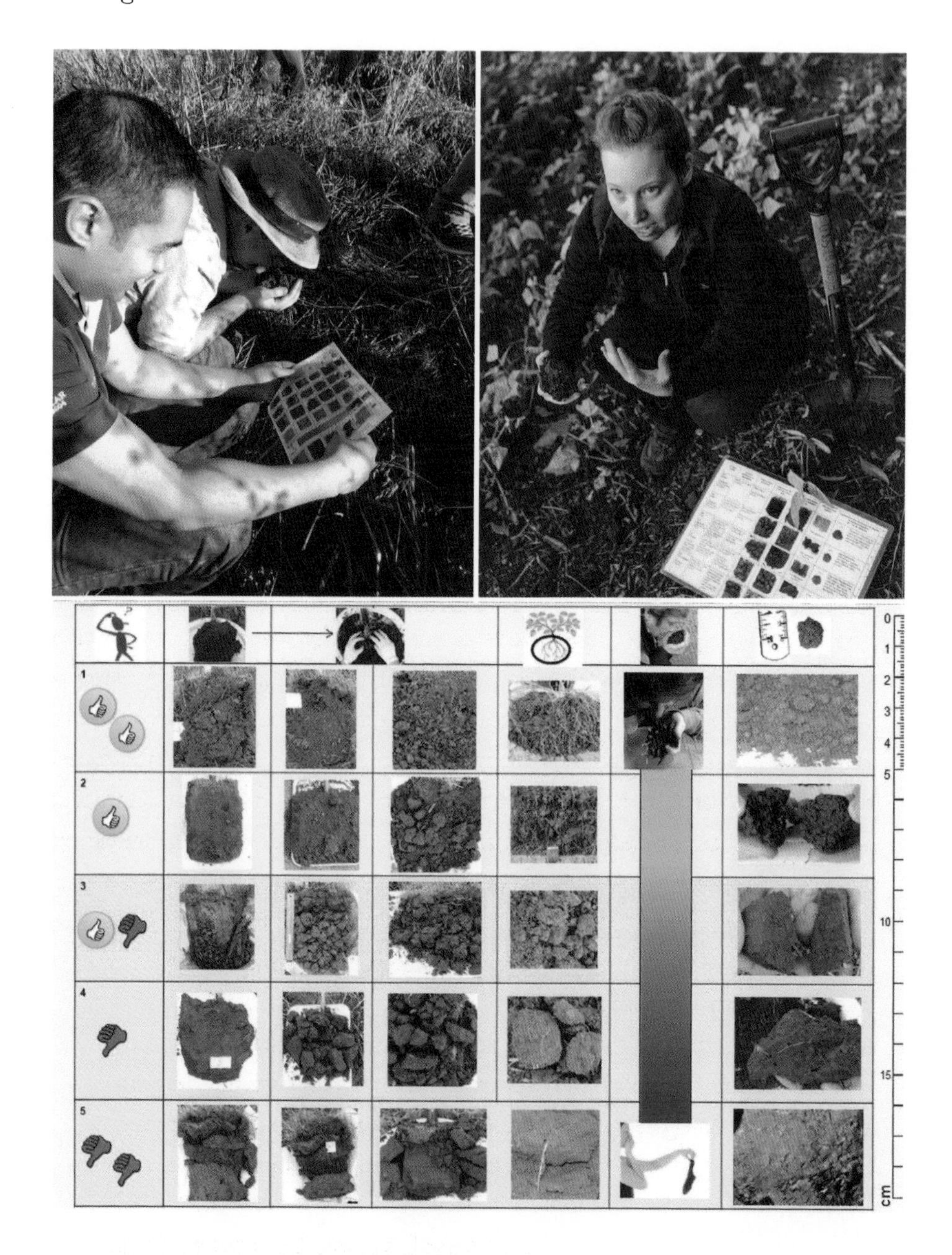

Diagnosing Soil Health using Visual Evaluation of Soil Structure (VESS)

Student farmers (top left image) being trained by **Associate Professor Rachel Guimarães** *(top right image) in the use of the Visual Evaluation of Soil Structure (VESS) using* *a visual key (lower image). Rachel is one of the pioneers of VESS (and a former student of mine) who is developing it for general use in Tropical and Sub-tropical climates by consultants, farmers and students. Her work includes describing the health of forest soils and reclaimed soils of the Amazon*[14]*. She is teaching in a no-tilled field of beans on an Oxisol, a common soil of high clay content in Brazil. No-till is widely-used in Brazil because the minimum soil disturbance and presence of surface residues helps to control water erosion. The upper two images are © Rachel Guimarães and are reproduced with permission.*

The Visual Evaluation of Soil Structure allows estimation of soil health from a spadeful of soil using a visual key and simple instructions[15]. The conservation of good soil health is important for agriculture, climate change and ultimately human health so that we have a collective responsibility to know it. I originally identified a need for such a simple photographic guide for describing the physical health of soil for organic farmers. This was highly relevant to them because good physical health is particularly important as the soil has to work effectively to support a crop in the absence of synthetic fertiliser. I led a group of international researchers and consultants in developing two versions of VESS, one for topsoil and one for subsoil. These young farmers from Brazil (top left image) are using VESS to learn how to score topsoil health on a scale of 1 (very good) to 5 (poor). They compare field soil with example pictures and descriptions (including soil smell) of each grade of health in a key, shown in the lower image and reproduced in a descriptive version at the back of this book. The farmers gently break up the larger aggregates of the soil along natural crack lines into smaller aggregates. These are then split to reveal the porosity and the roots within. The arrangement of porosity and aggregates is

> *“Through VESS people can understand how soil can affect human health and therefore appreciate that soil conservation is the responsibility of everyone”*

the soil structure and the pictures show typical soil structures. The chart is simple and readily understood. Note that a more complete assessment of soil health may need other measurements such as soil acidity (pH), nutrient status or suspected contaminants.

Rachel sees VESS as helping to promote and conserve soil health in degraded soybean/maize, sugar cane and crop livestock production areas in Brazil. She believes that 'VESS is easily learned making it a tool that is accessible to the whole population, helping people get in contact with the soil. She thinks that through VESS people can understand how soil can affect human health and therefore appreciate that soil conservation is the responsibility of everyone'.

Healthy food from healthy soil

This image shows potatoes growing in a thick, fertile, humus-rich topsoil in Switzerland. The soil is derived from parent material left behind after glaciers retreated about 10 000 years ago. A typical harvest is a generous 4 kilograms of potatoes per square metre[16]. The image is © Agroscope (Gabriela Brändle, Urs Zihlmann), LANAT (Andreas Chervet).

In continuing to receive the many benefits from soil we need to keep the soil itself fertile and healthy with sufficient porosity and organic matter to support a wide microbial biodiversity and the development of humus. Soil biodiversity can be maintained and restored by sustainable land management and is an underused means of improving soil health[17].

One of the pioneers of organic agriculture, Sir Albert Howard, recognised that 'the health of soil, plant, animal and man is one and indivisible'[18].

Part II. Healthy planet

Soil influences our planetary health mainly through the consequences of its use for agriculture and food production. Agriculture occupies nearly 40% of global land. Food production from agriculture produces approximately 34% of global greenhouse gas emissions[1] and uses 70% of freshwater, mainly for irrigation[2]. This huge area of agricultural ecosystems needs to be made more sustainable and any further conversion of land to agriculture should be avoided to prevent massive biodiversity loss[2]. The global food system is also the single biggest contributor to deforestation, drought, freshwater pollution and the collapse of aquatic wildlife[3,4]. Farmers and their choice of agricultural methods are thus very important for sustaining our planetary health as well as soil health and human health.

In this section I show the importance of some of the many critical functions that soils provide us – from supporting our water system to combatting climate change. Next, I describe how soil is being damaged and degraded by intensive agriculture and food choices and show that soil recovery is essential to our planet's health.

Agroecology is a group of alternative farming systems to intensive agriculture that allow soil recovery partly because of improved soil management. I describe several examples of such alternative systems along with the associated improved soil health that is vital for planetary health.

While agroecology is largely a farming technique, we can adopt its principles in our food choices e.g. eating less meat and more food produced by agroecology. I introduce several agroecological systems that illustrate the role that good soil management has in making agriculture more environmentally sustainable while permitting the production of nutritious food of good quality[5,6].

Water of Life

Without soil, water runs to waste through our hands.

Water is one of our key global resources and the decline in its availability is so steep that it has been identified as one of the greatest global catastrophic risks by the Commission for the Human Future[7]. Soil is an important store for water. For example, Scotland's soils hold more water in total than all of its freshwaters – lochs, rivers and streams combined.

“ *Without soil, water runs to waste through our hands* ”

The ability to store water varies between soils. The more organic matter in the soil, and the better the soil structure, then the more water can be stored. Organic matter helps to improve the number of medium-sized porosity spaces that can hold water. For every 1% increase in soil carbon, an acre of land can hold an additional 180,000 litres of water.

Peaty soils are composed of over 50% organic matter and can hold large amounts of water. Many of the soils of Scotland are peaty and have good structure. Water stored in these soils often flows to our streams and reservoirs. The water stored in all soils directly supplies plants and many creatures. Dissolved nutrients from the soil are transported in this water to plants and soil microbes. When the soil water storage is full, the water runs off over the soil surface taking with it soil particles and dissolved nutrients – leading to flooding and potential pollution.

The soil also purifies water. Remarkably, soil is earth's largest natural water filter[8]. Water is purified by physically screening out particles, storing pollutants within clay particles and decomposing pollutants through the action of microbes[8]. The type and content of organic matter is important in how well the water is purified and how it tastes. In my parents' first croft[9] in North-east Scotland we had a spring that ran off natural peaty soil. It provided the most delicious water we had ever tasted and I'm sure it helped to keep us all healthy.

Healthy soil is vital for regulating the availability and quality of our drinking water.

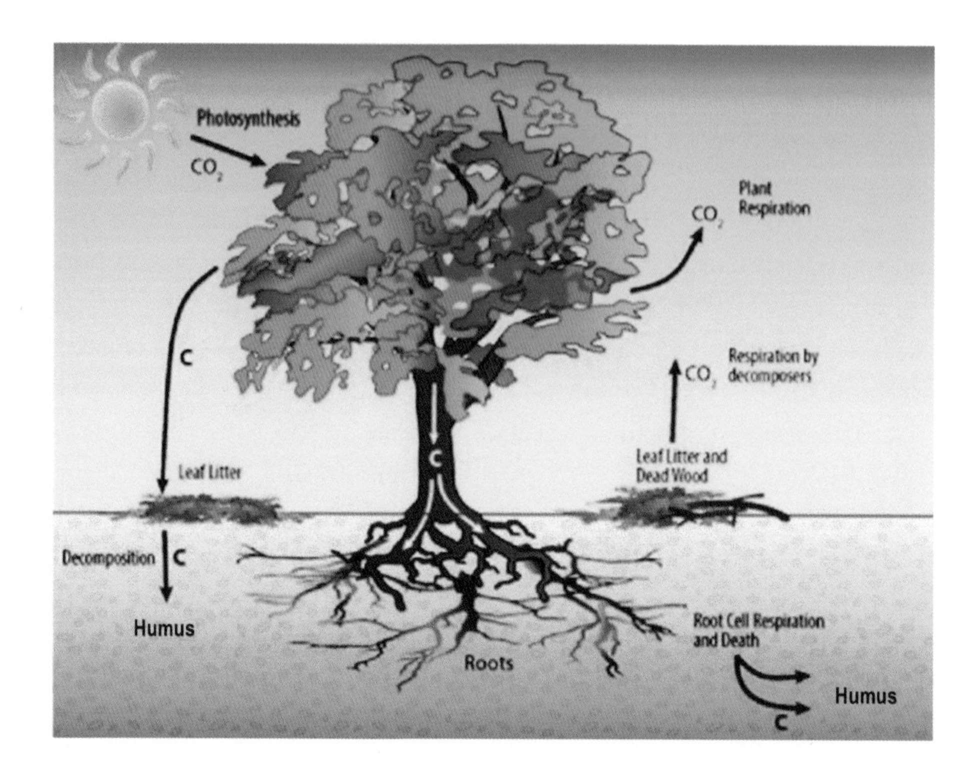

Storing carbon in the soil: capturing climate change

This diagram shows how carbon (C) from the atmosphere enters and exits the soil during plant growth and how some is stored in the soil, forming a cycle. Source: Valerie Martin, Technical Education Research Centre (TERC), Creative Commons.

Carbon dioxide (CO_2) is absorbed by plants and turned into carbohydrates through photosynthesis, creating leaves, wood and roots. These organic materials accumulate on or are buried in the soil forming soil organic matter that temporarily stores carbon from the atmosphere – organic matter contains 60–70% carbon. At the end of the growing season the soil organic matter decomposes as it is eaten by soil microbes and fungi that then respire carbon dioxide back into the atmosphere. However not all of the carbon is sent back into the atmosphere this way, some resists decomposition and is made into stable or protected forms that act as a longer-term store of carbon. These forms are collectively know as humus, making the soil an important sink for atmospheric carbon dioxide[10]. Humus is also a valuable material for binding together soil particles into a stable structure and for storing soil water.

Soil health is heavily dependent on the content of organic matter. Addition of organic material can help restore a degraded soil to good health, but this needs to be maintained. Organic material needs to be constantly added to the soil to make up for what is being slowly lost. It is usually beneficial to increase the organic matter content as this increases the storage of atmospheric carbon dioxide as humus.

> “*The soil is an important sink for atmospheric carbon dioxide*”

In these ways soil organic matter plays an integral role in storing carbon dioxide and in conserving soil health. Without regular additions of organic material to soil, we are, yet again, contributing to the degradation of our environment and planet.

In my garden, I'm regularly surprised at how quickly muck, compost or, best of all, a winter cover crop along with rain and frost create a good, friable structure in the topsoil that allows the growth of healthy veggies. These vegetables need other key nutrients held in the soil – notably nitrogen.

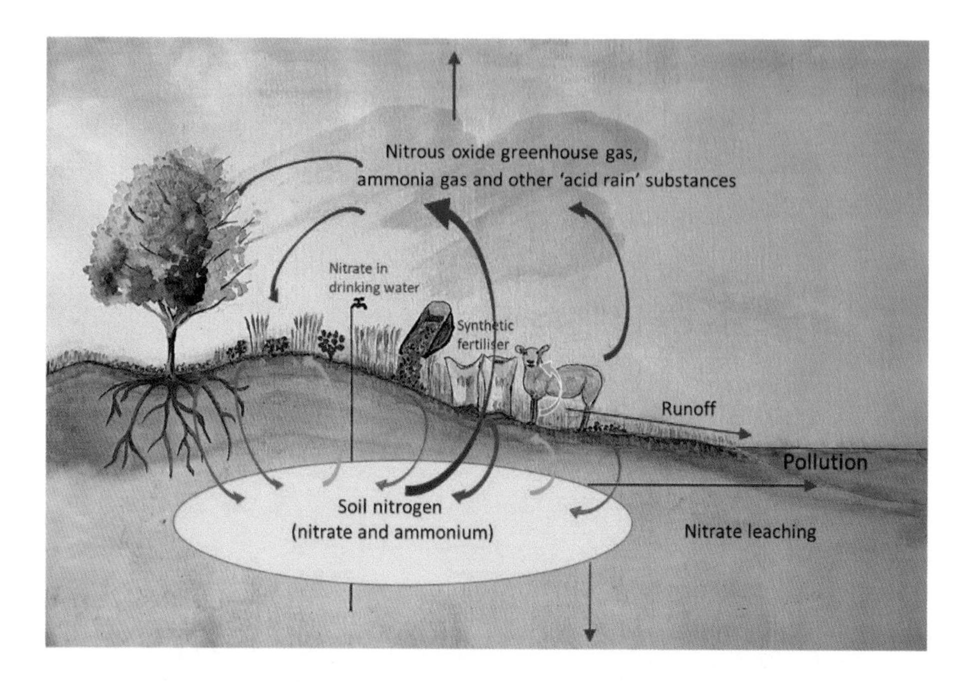

Nitrogen: from greening power to global warming

Nitrogen is the key nutrient for plant growth, essential for greening power. The soil controls how it cycles through plants and the environment. Here the text and arrows that represent the changes in chemistry of the way that nitrogen is cycled in our environment are superimposed on a watercolour image of a section of an agricultural landscape.

Nitrogen gas is present in the air and it is within us and all living beings. It ranks with carbon and oxygen as a key element of life. Nitrogen gas from the atmosphere needs to be converted to nitrate or ammonium to form a soil nitrogen source suitable for uptake by plant roots. Soil nitrogen becomes available naturally during the decomposition of plant residues, especially from legume roots such as clover and peas that act like fertiliser (brown arrows). This, along with animal manure, are the main sources of soil nitrogen for organic farming. More intensive types of agriculture rely on synthetic fertiliser to build the soil nitrogen source. Synthetic fertiliser production is very energy intensive, the equivalent of 170 litres of fossil fuel is required to fertilise one hectare of agricultural land and is a large contribution to the energy required for food production. It can also be a large financial input for farmers when energy prices are high.

Nitrogen fertiliser is powerful: the more that is applied to grass and leafy vegetables, the greener and thicker they grow. Such nitrogen has boosted crop yields greatly over the last 60–70 years and is important for food production in intensive farming. However, typically only 25 to 50% of applied synthetic nitrogen fertiliser is actually used by arable crops[11] with the remainder lost as the powerful greenhouse gas nitrous oxide, as ammonia present in droplets of water and as nitrate leaching to fresh water or to the soil water (red arrows).

Nitrous oxide escaping from the land is a long-lived greenhouse gas that is almost 300 times more potent than CO_2 over a 100-year period. It also contributes to the destruction of the protective ozone layer in the stratosphere[12] – greening power gone ballistic. This means that the world's use of synthetic nitrogen fertilisers in agriculture could threaten efforts to keep global warming below 2°C above pre-industrial levels[13], the threshold beyond which climate change risks become unacceptably high.

Long distance transport in the atmosphere of ammonia gas or ammonium particles can lead to deposition on plants and soils as 'acid rain' resulting in acid conditions, damage to trees, decreased plant biodiversity and acidified soils[14].

Nitrate leaching as runoff over the soil can lead to pollution of lakes and rivers causing dense growth of plants and green algae – greening power appearing in the wrong place. Nitrates can leach downwards through the soil into zones tapped for drinking water both for animals and human beings. The soil cannot readily remove nitrate so it persists as a contaminant.

Agriculture and the rest of the food supply chain create 32% of acidifying emissions of nitrogen and sulphur airborne particles and 78% of leached chemicals that cause water pollution.

The creation of synthetic fertiliser allows us to produce cheap food via intensive agriculture when energy is also cheap. However, the degradation of the environment through the energy used to make it and through the production of pollutants in its use can be substantial.

Industrial agriculture: liable to soil and environmental degradation

In a humid climate, a degraded soil becomes easily waterlogged after heavy rains thereby delaying the potato harvest – food that is hard to remove from unhealthy soil. In all climates such soil can't hold enough water early in the season for good crop yields. Soil is degraded here by destruction of the soil structure by compaction and disruption by machinery that diminishes porosity and reduces the soil's ability to absorb and drain water. This prevents the farmer from getting on to the soil to harvest it without causing further damage, as shown in this image. Water has run off over the surface and taken eroded soil with it.

Under industrial (intensive) agriculture large areas of land require a lot of synthetic fertilisers and pesticides to grow crops of cereals, soy and potatoes, many of which are used to feed animals in intensive production of meat and milk. This has resulted in degradation of the soil that reduces crop productivity and the quality of the nutrition of our food and hence the security of our food supply[15]. In dry conditions in developing countries, soil degradation is an important reason for droughts causing famine. Degraded soils can't hold much rain water.

Industrial agriculture is vulnerable to climate change and the increasing cost and scarcity of fertilisers and fuel[16]. Sources of phosphorus fertiliser are dwindling. Fertilisers are important nutrients that farmers add every year. Climate change is also having a direct effect of making weather more extreme in one third of farmed areas such that they no longer support adequate crop production and are outside of the 'safe climatic space'[17]. Safe climatic space refers to the climatic conditions where most of the global food production has historically developed and where crops are adapted to it. Without large cuts in emissions of greenhouse gases, Cambodia, Ghana and India could be left out of the safe climatic space mainly because of higher temperatures and drought[17].

> *One third of areas of global food production (are moving) outside of the 'safe climatic space'*

The type of food that we choose and its means of production influence the environmental impact of our diet[18]. It is well known that beef has a higher climate footprint than other meats, particularly from industrial agriculture. Meat and other animal products produce over half of the greenhouse gas emissions from food, yet only provide one fifth of the total calories that we eat and drink. Moving to a diet that excludes many animal products would bring substantial environmental benefits and reduce the amount of land needed to produce our food[4,18], freeing up land to actively store carbon[2].

My own diet includes some meat. I am a demitarian. At a meeting as part of a large European Union project researching the influence of synthetic fertiliser application on the environment, I adopted the recommendations of the Barsac Declaration[19]. This basically means choosing to eat half as much meat and fish as previously thus 'making meat special'. Widespread adoption of this 'option of medium ambition' would reduce air-borne nitrogen pollutants, reduce greenhouse gas emissions, reduce nitrogen and phosphorus pollutants to water[19] and reduce the area of land needed for food production.

The benefits of reducing meat eating are further improved by choosing our food from more sustainable production systems such as organic farming. This would significantly reduce the environmental impacts of eating meat and fish[19]. We need to make a transition to more resilient, economical and climate-proof cropping systems that feed us while recycling nutrients and conserving soil health. Such resilient agricultural systems are important in maintaining the continuity of our food supplies in all parts of the world and are vital for planetary health, social stability and, of course, reliable food production[20].

Agroecology: sustainable agriculture with soil at its heart

Earthworms pull straw into their burrows and digest it with soil to produce highly fertile worm casts that are sometimes taken up and deposited at the soil surface as shown here. Such natural soil mixing is best encouraged in soil that is left undisturbed. This is called a no-tillage approach. This increases soil organic matter and stores carbon as humus thus mitigating climate change[21]. The humble worm can help tackle global warming! Sustainable soil management like this also increases soil porosity, improving the ability of the soil to store and to drain water and to keep plant roots well aerated, thus reducing the emissions of powerful greenhouse gases such as nitrous oxide and methane[12]. The net effect is to improve soil health and this is a vital route to tackling problems of food security, global change and environmental degradation[22].

Agroecology is agriculture that harnesses natural principles of plant growth, producing food that makes the best use of natural resources without damaging them. Such agriculture phases out the use of synthetic fertilisers and pesticides, uses extensive grasslands and brings diverse farms and mosaic landscapes[23,24]. Widespread adoption of agroecology would provide fewer animal products (of higher quality) and more fruit and vegetables giving healthier food than industrial agriculture[24]. Agroecology also reduces the global warming effect of agriculture by increasing the potential for carbon sequestration and curbing use of synthetic nitrogen fertiliser. It is also about two to four times more energy efficient than conventional intensive farming due to reduced use of fossil fuels and fertilisers[23].

> *"Agroecology produces food that makes the best use of natural resources without damaging them"*

Here the use of the term agroecology includes the similar techniques of regenerative agriculture[25] and conservation agriculture[26] that are based on similar principles.

Agroecology also provides some of the practices in climate-smart agriculture[27]. Agriculture needs to adapt to mitigate the impact of climate change. Industrial agriculture practices with large fields of uniform crops are vulnerable to extreme weather and shifts in climate. Some of the best ways for farmers to increase resilience to climate change include adopting agroecological practices such as growing a range of different crops, including trees and animals, water conservation and building soil organic matter[28].

Agroecology embraces the three main principles of sustainable soil management. These are disturbing the soil as little as possible, growing crops that stay in the soil for long periods and mixing in crop residues to keep the soil covered and maximise recycling. Such principles usually need a variety of crops in a rotation[29]. Some, if not all, of these principles need to be extended to all agricultural systems. **Professor Rattan Lal**, one of the world's greatest soil management experts, pointed out the importance of sustainable soil management of soil health for achieving the Sustainable Development Goals of the United Nations for 2030. These include ending poverty, zero hunger and good health and well-being[30].

I think that a vital aspect of improving soil management is the use of natural means to strengthen the soil's greening power. Examples are preserving good porosity by minimising compaction and sowing densely rooted crops and sowing cover crops that fix atmospheric nitrogen naturally and conserve it during rainfall.

Conservation agriculture: protecting the soil

Two methods of establishing cereal crops using conservation agriculture are shown. In the top image seeds were being sown directly into the soil (no-tillage) that was free from compaction by wheels, using a tractor that straddles the sown area. The lower image shows a cover crop being flattened and maize being no-tilled directly into it; the cover crop helps suppress weeds and protects the emerging crop. The image is © the periodical 'No-till farmer'.

Conservation agriculture is an important part of sustainable soil management. It ensures minimal soil disturbance by using no-tillage and/or a permanent soil cover (mulch). Between 1980 and 2000, I tested several systems of conservation agriculture in Scotland with colleagues Dr Brennan Soane and Mike O'Sullivan, compaction specialists; control of soil compaction was particularly important for success[31].

These techniques all keep crop residues at the surface, which conserve and protect the soil and help to preserve soil fertility. No-tillage can improve water infiltration into the soil, reducing runoff and soil loss by erosion[32]. These techniques are best used as part of an integrated agroecological system.

Organic farming: improving soil and human health

Organic horticulture in Hawke's Bay province, New Zealand, where soils are highly productive and the water is pure. These crop rows use the principles of permaculture and are oriented for favourable solar access, rainfall and slope. The rows follow the contour of the land to catch the water from rainfall or irrigation. These are in-ground beds where compost and mulch are added in situ rather than in raised beds[33].

Organic farming is an agroecological system that avoids the use of synthetic fertilisers, generally increasing soil quality. These increases are detectable by visual soil description techniques[34]. Organically grown fruit and vegetables have been shown to contain higher levels of health-promoting phytochemicals than conventional produce[35].

Organic farming systems provide food at the local scale. They operate well in urban agriculture in areas where human health is often run-down and well-being is sustained by communal activity and by the access to fresh produce[36,37].

At a larger scale, organic farming has crop rotations including crops that accumulate nitrogen in their roots (e.g. clover) that is passed on to the next crop. There are often mixed rotations of crops and grass that involve animals. Organic farming is holistic, with the emphasis on the connection between soil, crop, animal, producer and customer and how the health of all of these is inextricably linked[38].

Organic farms can provide profound healing for those who work them. In Washington, US, is 'Growing Veterans', an organic farm for women and men who have returned from combat with problems such as depression or post-traumatic stress disorder. Here they are given opportunities to reintegrate into society through employment, professional volunteering or simply communication with other veterans. They know 'the joy, frustration and ultimate satisfaction that comes from coaxing food from the earth'. A humbling statement from one veteran is 'it feels really good to be putting something in dirt (sic) that is going to grow and isn't going to explode and kill someone'[39].

“*Vulnerable people and degraded soils need time to recover*”

Soil recovery usually involves long-term improvement in structure by good soil management involving soil loosening as necessary and sowing crops with roots that loosen the soil and gradually increase porosity and humus. Both are natural processes. In a similar way I think that natural processes of careful nurture by sympathetic people in the long term is needed for the recovery of people from mental health problems. Vulnerable people and degraded soils need time to recover.

A spadeful of topsoil from intensively-managed pasture that has been heavily compacted by repeated trampling by cattle, North Island, New Zealand.

Nearby soil that is recovering its health as a result of better control of grazing and use of slow nitrogen release fertilisers.

Agroecological principles recover soil health in intensive dairy production

Soil health-promoting techniques work within industrial farming methods. For example, milk production is crucial to the success of the New Zealand economy. The grass is intensively grazed and high levels of synthetic nitrogen fertiliser are typically added. This can result in heavy soil compaction by animal treading and poor aeration, shown in the top picture. In this image below, **Dr Graham Shepherd***, a scientist pioneering the use of visual estimates of soil health to guide soil-friendly agriculture*[40]*, is holding a compacted soil that is recovering. Use of controlled access of the grazing cows and lesser amounts of more sustainable fertilisers and pasture seed mixtures has renewed earthworm and root activity that has allowed the creation of large pores. The change of colour from grey to brown indicates that soil biological conditions and soil health have improved. Graham stated that this image showing evidence of degraded soil recovering should be seen, not only be farmers, but by the world. Reducing the intensity of agriculture can allow a soil to recover while conserving the environment and productivity.*

I believe that the idea of recovery is vital both for degraded or vulnerable soils and for hurt and vulnerable humans. Both require natural methods and proceed slowly at Nature's pace. Recovery is only partly helped by use of technology and chemical fixes. This theme appears again later in the book.

Well-fed dairy cows improve planetary health

Meet **Dr Paul Hargreaves**, *a soil pasture expert working with the prestigious SRUC (Scotland's Rural College) Langhill Dairy Herd in south-west Scotland. He is frequently to be seen – as here – with a soil auger in his hand.*

Paul states 'Provided that grazing conditions are good, animals have an important role to play in converting grass – a good crop for conserving soil health – into protein. High quality milk and meat provide calcium, protein and minerals for health. It has been regularly shown that a grass-based diet is both healthy for the cows, plus produces a more quality milk. A healthy soil is the basis of this with the soil chemistry, biology and physics all supporting the grass production. Appropriate diets for dairy cows, that include some concentrate feed, increase the efficiency of conversion and reduce

> *“Animals have an important role to play in converting grass – good for conserving soil health – into protein”*

methane production from the animals and hence their contribution to climate change[41].

Rotational grazing of grasses of a variety of species and containing pasture herbs, such as chicory or sheeps parsley, is particularly useful for encouraging root growth, helping to conserve carbon and to improve soil health. Improvements are considered to be best when grazing is of short duration, with long periods of pasture rest giving dense growth – a technique known as mob grazing because of the high number of cattle on fairly small areas. These types of grazing enable the soil to absorb heavy rainfall and reduce flooding, useful for moderating the effects of climate change[42].

In contrast, more intensive grazing reduces the microporosity through soil compaction and increases the proportion of water held in the soil porosity and encourages less efficient microbes in the soil; these produce more greenhouse gases, especially nitrous oxide. As the balance of the physical aspects of the soil shifts to be less favourable: it affects the biology and chemistry, allowing increased production of greenhouse gases – an example of poor soil health leading to further environmental problems[43].' Holistically managed grazing of livestock is considered a key management tool to restoring the world's grassland soils, reversing desertification and increasing the soil sink for organic carbon[44].

Paul continues: 'it is ironic that in many agricultural systems, the arable farms are in desperate need of organic manure to maintain the soil organic matter and soil quality, while the livestock farms have problems using the slurry and manure from housed stock and treat these as wastes.

Further, appropriate use of organic manures could help substantially to store atmospheric carbon in the land[45] and avoid greenhouse gas emissions thereby providing a substantial fraction of the most cost-effective 'natural climate solutions' to maintain global warming under 2 degrees C by 2030[46].'

Paul is helping to develop VESS (Visual Evaluation of Soil Structure) and other soil analyses to monitor the improvements in the cattle pastures with a view to minimising greenhouse gas emissions and making best use of the plant nutrients in his organic manures.

Soil with compact layer above 0.15 m depth that required shallow loosening before cropping

Soil with compact layer below 0.15 m depth that required loosening to 0.25 m depth before cropping

Soil structure improving under grass plus clover and grazing animals in an organic rotation

A well-structured soil that allows no-tillage to succeed

Using VESS to monitor improving soil health

The Visual Evaluation of Soil Structure (VESS) method can be used to assess any soil system and help guide beneficial soil management decisions. During a VESS assessment soil layers are broken-up by hand as shown above. Knowledge of the location in the field of compact layers and their depths enables these areas to be targeted for improvement by loosening by tillage before adopting conservation agriculture. These examples are from medium-heavy textured soils in South Scotland.

The handling and observation of soil does more than reveal soil health. It reminds all of us of the need for stewardship and of the power of the soil – its greening power – as a living organism, to produce our food. We appreciate the richness of the soil and its productive ability, though we similarly realise its vulnerability to abuse. Handling soil usually results in dirty hands; we need more people to get their hands dirty in caring for our planet.

> *"Simple tools like VESS can shift the focus of agronomy onto the soil more"*

Looking forwards, **Dr Joanna Cloy**, a leading researcher in soils and environmental science, sees a great future for VESS, 'I think that simple tools like VESS can be extended to shift the focus of agronomy onto the soil more. Especially when visual assessments of soil structural quality are combined alongside visual assessments of crop vigour and performance, plant rooting depth and earthworm counts. Soil guidance using VESS is particularly useful for agroecology and regenerative agriculture techniques such as mob grazing. The VESS technique, especially the alternative 'VESS without words' chart recently developed, also shows promise in developing countries, for example, in Africa where it can provide an affordable method of assessing soil quality that can be used by many from schoolchildren to scientists[47].'

I am happy still to be helping Joanna and Paul and their colleagues from the UK and beyond in developing VESS systems and bringing the basic awareness of soil to consultants, farmers, students and children from all over the globe. Since starting to develop VESS over 20 years ago, I have probably made well over a thousand soil assessments. To this day, every time that I dig out a fresh sample of soil for assessment, I feel the wonder of the soil and almost always discover some new aspect of it. In my mind, experiencing that wonder results from the simple training in soil observation provided by the VESS chart.

Agroecology in practice: building on traditional wisdom

Brian Muirden, *a friend and farmer from my home village of Clatt, with his plough. The plough is often maligned but, under appropriate conditions, is actually a relatively gentle form of cultivation, inverting and loosening the soil and spreading residues and soil organisms throughout the topsoil. Most organic farmers depend on ploughing for incorporating nitrogen-rich residues from the surface thereby maintaining fertility. Ploughing may even be used occasionally in conservation agriculture to restore soil degraded by extreme weather. Recently, I was passenger with Brian as he ploughed. Suddenly, I was pitched forward and banged my head on the roof as he slammed on the brakes. He had spotted a nest of field mice and stopped to move them to safety. Caring for Nature comes naturally to most working farmers.*

“ *Caring for Nature comes naturally to most working farmers* ”

Brian has worked the family farms for over 50 years. His traditional approach to farming crops (barley and turnips) and livestock (cattle and sheep on grass), with emphasis on crop rotation and recycling of animal wastes to the land, has sustained his soils sufficiently to maintain good productivity over many years. As elsewhere in the UK, market conditions and social changes have resulted in a decrease in the numbers of farmers and farm workers so that personal productivity has had to increase to maintain income. In effect, Brian has gradually moved from a system that we would have recognised as agroecological to one that is more intensive. This has resulted in the amalgamation of small fields and farms having to be merged to allow larger machinery and more pesticides to be used on a less diverse range of crops. As a consequence, bird types and numbers and some native vegetation species have decreased. This has happened throughout the UK, reducing biodiversity and the beauty of the landscape[48]. Nevertheless, Brian uses chemicals and synthetic fertilisers sparingly so that his system has some similarity to organics; such 'organic-ish' systems are what some believe conventional farming systems need to move towards to give greater sustainability with better soil and livestock health[29].

Brian sticks with his system because it reliably delivers sufficient income year on year and the soil quality is mostly fine. Surprisingly to me, Brian, like other colleagues with a good knowledge of the land, learned a lot about maintaining soil health using VESS and other soils information[49]. He studies the ground more and is increasingly aware of the need to control compaction by his field machines and to maintain organic matter by ploughing-in residues of crops and manure. He also uses fallow periods to allow a soil depleted of minerals or subjected to compaction to recuperate.

He thinks that adopting conservation agriculture in his system is risky – a feeling shared by many older farmers in the current market situation. Nevertheless, the more frequent extreme weather and the prospect of more expensive inputs and different financial support schemes makes farmers increasingly open to the greater sustainability of conservation agriculture and agroecological techniques.

The high point of the farming year in Clatt is harvest time especially as the evening light dims and the drone of the combine harvesters comes and goes. The fertile, floury scent of the threshed barley and cut straw brings a slight dryness to the mouth and the land is studded with the crawling lights of the harvesting machinery. Somehow you feel wonderfully enveloped in the essence of creation, fulfilment and the cycle of survival.

Innovation in agroecology: soil centrism

Meet **Douglas Christie** *with his healthy organic animals and no-tilled soil. He has pioneered novel approaches to agroecology at his farm in Fife, east Scotland. Like Brian, he has coped with working with limited labour resources.*

Douglas says: 'Soil is really the primary asset that holds us all together, it is the kingpin of the whole equation. Our farming approach is 'soil-centric' to ensure both profitability and sustainability. We use organic production for our beef herd and conservation agriculture (mainly no-till) for cereal cropping. Cover crops help both to protect the soil and to reduce pesticide use. Our crop mixtures provide nutritious fodder and attract a diversity of insects and birds. My soils are dark with humus, rich in worms and are well-structured with strong, stable aggregates. This increased soil resilience is helping to future-proof the farm.'

“ *Soil is really the primary asset that holds us all together* ”

He is not just an innovator, he is also a teacher. Changing his farming system was not easy and he regularly invites colleagues and students to his farm to share his experiences. Furthermore, like many progressive farmers, he uses social media to publicise his outcomes and ideas (Twitter @DouglasChristi9).

“ *Our farming approach is 'soil-centric' to ensure both profitability and sustainability* ”

His farm overlooks the Firth of Forth, near Edinburgh. From personal experience, looking across his fields full of diverse flowering crops buzzing with pollinators towards the sea on a sunny day is a true tonic to the senses.

Agroforestry and companion cropping: diversity in action

Agroforestry at Masaka District, Uganda. Trees are grown interspersed with crops, typically bananas, cassava, beans, vegetables, maize and coffee. Agroforestry is used here to enable efficient, secure use of limited land resources and improvement in soil fertility. Image used according to the Creative Commons Attribution-Share Alike 3.0 Unported license.

Agroforestry is an agroecological system where trees and agricultural or horticultural crops are grown together on the same land[50]. Nutrients are cycled and shared between crops and trees not only in the root system but also through the leaves falling on to the ground surface. The trees provide shelter and help to keep nutrients and water in the system. This cooperation also stabilises the soil, improves wildlife and helps to tackle climate change. It is also popular for animal grazing as the trees provide feed and shelter. Agroforestry does have problems in being labour intensive and there being a long lag time before trees are fully grown. Similar principles bring the advantages of intercropping where two or more crops are grown together in strips or rows. Companion cropping involves crops grown together to exploit mutually beneficial relationships between plants such as improved pest resistance, improved flavour or better growth[51]. A common example is the growth of clover with cereals to build up a reserve of fixed nitrogen – customary in organic farming.

On a large scale, agroforestry is used in an ambitious initiative to combat desertification in the Sahel, the savannah area just south of the Sahara Desert. A 10-mile wide strip of trees was planted across the width of Africa, a distance of over 4,300 miles. Unfortunately, many trees died in the arid conditions as desertification continued. The local farmers had a better idea of cropping by using an agroforestry system that is based around modified traditional agricultural practices. Grids of planting pits and retaining walls were built to increase rainfall storage in the soil and to prevent water runoff. This nurtured the natural regeneration of native trees so that crops like millet and sorghum could be grown around them. This regreening of the Sahel is a great example of the success of grass-roots innovation[52].

Agroforestry can also help to tackle rural depopulation. In the Croft Woodlands Project in Scotland[53] new crofts can be created that involve the planting of new woodland or restoration of existing forestry among rough pasture. This aids in controlling climate change and increases the rural population, restoring life to sparsely populated areas. Many areas of Scotland are exposed to high winds and have few trees. Other strategies need to be developed by crofters to help sustain the population. I can vouch for this, having been brought up on a remote croft on the top of a hill in north-east Scotland where the wind seemed to be always blowing in several directions at once.

BLACKLAND: AGRICULTURE AT THE EDGE

How external factors modify soil structure and function

EARLY PERIOD

1860s + 50 years

Highest population 1863
Horse and human power

Arable rotation / lazybeds* + grazing
Cattle for home use and export
Labour on croft + part-time employment
Nutrients recycled

Drainage maintained and extended
Ploughing and cultivation
Knowledge accumulation

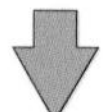

Increase in aeration
No excess vegetation

Soil becomes more friable
Increased microbial action

MODERN PERIOD

1960s + 50 years

Labour reduced by war and birth control. Transportation and fossil fuel use increase. Changes in agricultural payments

Rough grazing
Sheep export
Paid full-time employment
Nutrient loss

Drainage not maintained
Milk cow unnecessary, cultivation ceases
Loss of skills

Waterlogging
Moss and litter build up

Soil becomes wetter and colder, more acidic

*Lazybeds are built up beds for arable cultivation about 2.5 m wide, separated by furrows

Blackland: agriculture at the edge

Meet one of my former students, **Mary Norton Scherbatskoy**. *She has been working on croft land in the Outer Hebrides – which fell out of use 50 years ago – to learn its secrets and restore productivity for livestock.*

Mary explains: 'My croft at Scotvein, Grimsay is typical of other small places in Uist (Outer Hebrides), neglected or misunderstood by science and producers alike. Over time, I learned to listen to the land. I came to ask, why are we supposed to do all kinds of things to our land to make it do something it doesn't want to do? Why couldn't we make the best of what we've got already?

Ten years of practice and research led CEIA (Crofting Environment Improvement Association, a group of like-minded crofters) to reject our current classification as 'land suitable only for permanent grass or rough grazing'. We now call it 'blackland,' a kind of highly organic soil with its own character, history and management techniques. For centuries, blackland fields were cultivated in a corn / hay rotation and today can yield high-quality silage. Such crofts – typical of a kind of soil too often called 'peat' – supported thousands of people for hundreds of years. Many are now derelict, overgrown or overgrazed. What happened?

Soil is the basis of agriculture but is affected by outside forces from climate to policy to family choices. All of these have conspired against blackland soils since the Second World War.

In the flow chart, the left column shows how the actions of people on the land in the earlier period made our blackland work better. It was able to support fairly dense populations of families for hundreds of years. People ate and lived without high inputs and great mechanical power. Although 'marginal', it worked; people devised ways of productively managing their land.

The right column shows how blackland ceased to be productive in more recent times, resulting from changes in the relationship between people and their land. It's not that the land is 'infertile', but that human understanding of it slipped away, influenced by exterior forces.

This should make us wary of importing 'improved' strategies from other land types in search of 'more'. We need a deeper understanding of the land's character and capability before dismissing it as useless, or damaging it through misplaced intervention. CEIA aims to bring our land back to health and increase productivity, benefitting ourselves, our neighbours and our community.

Mary has been a great connecter with her crofting colleagues and with external helpers, fostering the sharing of knowledge and wisdom. To facilitate this, she used to help organise a yearly conference near Michaelmas Day. There are two types of large agricultural pests in Uist, deer and geese that calmly graze the precious grass. However, the crofters got their own back at the conference meals, where copious amounts of venison stew and goose pie were eaten!

More details of Mary's work on blackland are available at https://www.blacklandcentre.org/ and in her book 'My Land: an agricultural journey'[54].

TYFA : A SCENARIO FOR
AN AGRO-ECOLOGICAL EUROPE IN 2050

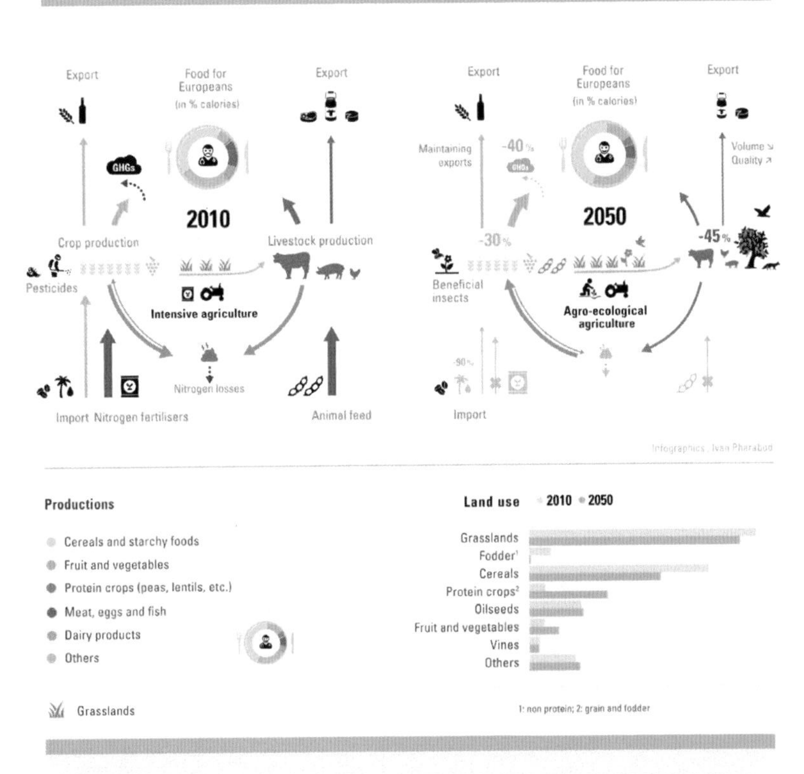

The TYFA scenario (Ten Years for Agroecology) is based on phasing out pesticides and synthetic fertilisers, redeploying natural grasslands and extending agro-ecological infrastructures (hedges, trees, ponds, stony habitats). It also envisages the generalisation of healthier diets containing fewer animal products and more fruit and vegetables. Despite a 35 % decline in production compared to 2010 (in kcal), this scenario meets the food needs of all Europeans while maintaining export capacity for cereals, dairy products and wine. It reduces agricultural sector greenhouse gas (GHG) emissions by 40 % compared to 2010, restores biodiversity and protects natural resources (soil life, water quality, more complex trophic chains).

Agroecology can sustain us

TYFA is the acronym for Ten Years for Agroecology, a project that is focused on driving organic farming in diverse family farms, phasing out pesticides and synthetic fertilisers and reducing the consumption of animal products, eating more fruit and vegetables and more plant protein instead, within the next decade. In spite of projecting a 35% reduction in overall production compared to 2010, this scenario would provide the food needs for the projected increased population of Europe along with the potential for food exports. This would also reduce energy used for making fertilisers, decrease greenhouse gas emissions from agriculture by 40% compared to 2010, restore biodiversity and preserve soil and water quality[24].

There are, of course, challenges in achieving such a change. The main requirement is a reduction in our consumption of animal products. This is not a withdrawal; ruminant animals allow a diverse, attractive landscape and help secure soil fertility without synthetic fertilisers. Indeed, when foods are ranked in terms of the density of nutrients that populations commonly lack globally, the top five are animal foods – with animal organ meat, such as liver, the best[55]. Change to more sustainable farming may need a combination of public pressure and a possible restructure of farming subsidies to reflect public health and cutting food costs by reducing marketing and advertising[56].

The options for agroecology in the previous pages demonstrate what is possible in a range of circumstances. Achieving success in adoption of novel techniques needs producers to be open to innovation and change, including modern technology. However, the success of such systems needs to include the experience and wisdom of the farmers currently working the land. No matter what is agreed, farmers need to be able to make a living and it is possible – as has been demonstrated in Africa[57]. Widespread adoption of agroecological systems in Africa with emphasis on recycling and conservation of nutrients could also help to stem the progressive loss of micronutrients on older soils[58].

The quality of soil and agronomic management is vitally important to the success of any agricultural system[59]. The sharing and discussion required to achieve this can occur by bringing farmers and advisors together around soil samples or soil pits with all getting their hands dirty. Agroecology is also a social movement with a strong ecological grounding that fosters justice, community, access, resilience, resistance and sustainability[60]. For these things to happen – and for all to realise the need to move to a more sustainable agriculture – we need a change of mindset and the soil provides lots of guidance if we look.

Part III. Healthy lives

The role that food has on our health is well-documented[1] – this can be seen as an indirect effect of soil on our health. But, the direct influence of soil on health is less well known. If we broaden our interpretation of health further, to include the comparison of soil with human properties and behaviour, then the link between soil and health is a concept that is almost hidden in folklore.

In this part I describe the influences of soil on health – either directly through contact or indirectly through food and medicines, gardening and meditation. The soil and how it works are then explored further with the help of the idea that the networking in soil is a model of the interconnected response needed to tackle world problems. I use examples of the parallels that can be drawn to show how we can start to build a better society and help achieve solutions to hunger, climate change and health. In this way, I show that motivation for action has to come from change deep within us, founded on spiritual activism and radical theology.

A vision of a world which operates in a way similar to the soil is suggested as a means to sustain human beings, the soil and the planet. All point to the need to recognise and heed the call of the soil, the call to care.

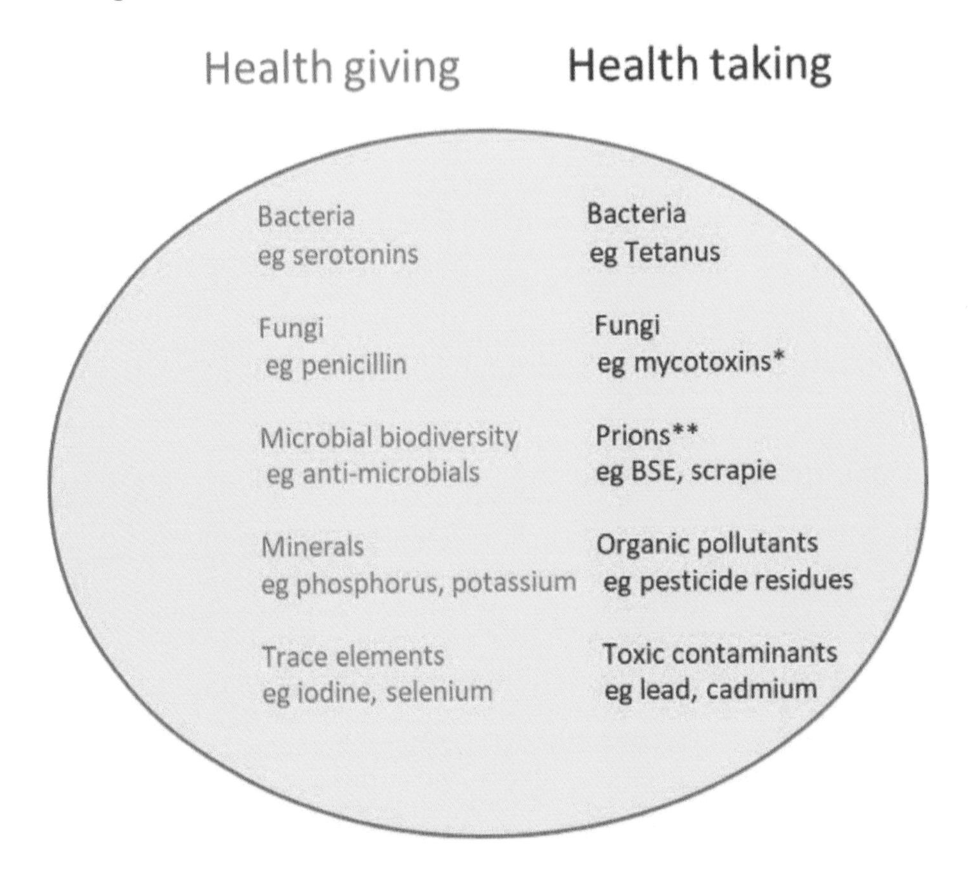

Human health and soil

Some soil organisms and chemicals that influence human health.

**Mycotoxins are produced by soil fungi and may be carcinogenic **Prions are types of protein that can trigger normal proteins in the brain to fold abnormally*

Soil contains organisms and properties that make it potentially a great asset for human health[2,3]. Some of these could be used as a base for antibiotics. For example, penicillin was derived from a fungus found in soil. Exposure to soil can reduce allergy development in children, possibly due to changes in the microbial composition and function in the gut improving the operation of the immune system[4]. In the recent Covid-19 pandemic, one of immunologist Dr Jenna Macciochi's recommendations to increase immune resistance was to eat vegetables as soon as possible after being taken from the field as these would contain traces of soil with bacteria that help build up the body's defence mechanisms[5]. Many of the organisms in soil are largely unknown and hold promise for developing 'anti-microbial' chemicals (to substitute for antibiotics), anti-cancer agents and natural anti-depressants. The solution to viral pandemics such as the Coronavirus[6] may even lie in there. I believe that this shows the need for more research into how soils can protect and improve human health[7].

Soil can also have negative effects on health – many are aware of the risk of catching tetanus from bacteria found in soil. Other effects are more related to soil chemical degradation by humans. Exposure to soil containing toxins such as arsenic or lead can lead to illness[7]. Soil pollution by industrial effluents and urban wastes can adversely affect human health[3]. In poor and deprived countries, soil transmits helminth infections when contaminated with infected faeces[8].

Nitrogen pollution can have profound and not well-known effects on human health. Algal blooms can be toxic leading to respiratory illnesses[9]. Nitrates leached into water stored deep in the soil and used for drinking can impact human health as thyroid disease, cancers and even 'blue-baby' syndrome in infants[9]. Emissions of ammonia gas can be transformed in the atmosphere to ammonium either attached to particles or dissolved in water droplets. This commonly occurs in combination with other pollutants from industry. Exposure to these particles can contribute to cardio-vascular disease-related mortality[10].

Soil also affects the quality and quantity of our food. The organisation Whole Health Agriculture (WHAg)) asserts that true health is dependent on the food that we eat, which is itself linked to the health of the entire farm that it comes from and to the wider environment[11]. This makes agriculture fundamental to human health. Nutrients in food are transferred from the soil to our food via crop roots. Trace elements – iodine, iron, selenium and zinc – are important for health. Shortages of these in our food due to deficiencies in the soil can have serious impact on well-being. Such deficiencies often occur due to depletion by excessive cropping. Trace elements are being progressively lost from older soils in less-developed countries such as India[12]. Such losses result from the failure to replace the micronutrients removed in the crops that have had their yields boosted in recent years due to the greater use of nitrogen fertilisers. For this reason, I take a multi-nutrient diet supplement regularly.

Pesticide residues in soil or on the surfaces of fruit and vegetables are unlikely to pose any health risks to consumers as regulation of pesticide use is very good in developed countries at least[13,14]. Nevertheless the influence of pesticides on food is difficult to resolve adequately. It is important for sustainability of food production, particularly through its influence on wildlife, to reduce the level of pesticides used in agriculture. See, for example, the Pesticide Action Network of Europe[15]. Another problem with some intensive livestock farming is the use of antibiotics in healthy animals to boost yields. These can persist as residues in animal-derived products which can contribute to antibiotic resistance, a serious health problem in the future[16].

Moving on, we have already discussed the benefits of handling soil for assessing soil health. Handling and touching soil also heal the mind.

Receiving energy from the soil

The benefits of human touch on healing are well-known. Touching a soil with healthy, loose aggregates teeming with life can calm and heal us.

An early example of healing by soil is found in the Bible where Jesus mixed the soil scraped from the ground with his spittle and smeared it on the eyes of a blind man. As **Alastair McIntosh** relates, this story also shows a need to heal our spiritual blindness[17].

Healing by direct soil contact that includes some spiritual input in the form of meditation occurs in grounding. Grounding involves standing still and composed on the soil to invigorate and relax the mind and body. Getting close to the soil by kneeling or lying on it brings the reality of the soil to you – sometimes quite sharply. As bestselling author Barbara Taylor[18] states, in this situation 'The body is a great reminder of where we came from and where we

> *"Handling and touching soils also heals the mind"*

are going, on the one sacred journey that we all make whether we mean to or not'. She is an enthusiast for walking barefoot on the soil. She sums up the spiritual importance of this rather beautifully: 'As long as you are on the earth and you know it, you are where you are supposed to be. You have everything you need to ground yourself in God.'[18].

Grounding can draw energy from the soil – an exercise for good weather! Bare feet are not essential for grounding though it is claimed that the direct connection between bare feet and earth allows the absorption of free electrons. These neutralise free radicals that can otherwise damage our cells[19].

T'ai Chi has movements based on ancient martial art poses that include grounding, these provide relaxation and overall health. Revitalisation of the body and mind involves receiving and conserving energy. T'ai Chi has sets of movements that can increase immune resistance[20].

However, most of us make physical contact with the soil during gardening.

The good of gardening

*My sister **Barbara** and her glorious garden in Huntly, North-east Scotland. She feels good when tending her flowers, when showing them to family and friends and when providing them with cuttings. Her garden proved particularly helpful during the recent Covid-19 epidemic when isolation was helped by getting out and getting her hands amongst the soil tending her plants; she calls them her 'bairns'.*

The contact with soil and plants during gardening, along with the physical activity in the fresh air, is good for mental health. Not only does it lift your spirits but there are physiological effects too – for example, the soil bacterium *Mycobacterium vaccae* is considered to activate brain cells to release more of the feel-good hormone serotonin[21]. These bacteria are released when working the soil. Sniff that soil and feel happy! The veggies and vases full of flowers are positive for health too. The garden is also a great topic of conversation for phone calls. I have spent many happy times talking to my sister about her bounteous garden.

Home gardening has been shown to give both physical and psychological benefits – and the more often you get out there the better for your health[22]. Also people with existing health issues benefit from the pleasure of gardening[22].

If you don't have a garden, community gardening can also improve social health, where working together helps people to develop and to bond[23]. Your town may even have community areas where free vegetables are grown by volunteers that you can eat and where you can learn to grow your own.

In the UK an important initiative for this local food production is the Incredible Edible Todmorden that has spread to a number of small towns and villages[24]. In Scotland, you can also participate in Therapeutic Gardening (Trellis Scotland)[25] – a network of 420 projects in garden spaces that are used to help people enhance their health and well-being. These support a range of gardeners from children in hospice care to older gardeners living in hospice accommodation.

If you haven't got time to look after your garden then let the weeds grow, start your own mini-forest, nurturing insects and wildlife with minimal effort. The weeds cover the soil like a protective skin, their roots stabilise it and the soil life can breathe – bringing healing[26]. This is better than bare soil and much better than soil smothered by bricks or cement or plastic turf. Please respect your neighbours, though – they may not like your dandelion heads floating over their garden!

At a larger scale, contacting the soil when working on a farm can bring healing and impact at a deeper, more spiritual level.

'I am proof of life after death
I am dawning from decay
my belly of mass graves
my open palms of gardens'

'I am evidence of love under fingernails
knee caps stained from kneeling to pray
sacred remains of yesterday
fertile with future'

'Take me in your palms
breathe in my memory
Remember me'

Restoring land and healing the oppressed

Soul Fire Farm is an 80-acre holding under organic horticulture near Albany in New York state. **Naima Penniman,** *shown in the top and bottom photographs, is the Program Director of the work of the Farm. The top and bottom images are © Naima Penniman, Soul Fire Farm. The middle image is from Leah Penniman's book[27], and is © Neshima Vitele-Penniman, Soul Fire Farm, The words are verses from Naima's outstanding poem 'Black Gold', published in Leah's book and are reproduced with permission.*

The farmland chosen for Soul Fire Farm was originally of marginal potential productivity due to the slope, the heavy clay soil and the reduced topsoil depth because of water erosion. With no access roads or buildings, it was all that could be afforded in 2006 by purchasers Leah Penniman and husband Jonah. They bought it because the people of colour where they lived in Albany had little access to nutritious food and they wanted good fruit and vegetables for themselves and for others in need. The land was returned to productivity by building up the soil using sheet composting, tarping (covering the soil to control weeds and increase residue decomposition) and terracing of sloping areas, assisted by many willing helpers.

The farm does so much more than supplying good food. It has become a place of training and refuge from violence and strife. Black, indigenous and people of colour come into contact with nature and especially with the soil. Many have lost their connection to the land because of its association with slavery and oppression. Here people can re-engage with the land with respect to their ancestors and through diverse means of worship and celebration. The restoration of organic matter to the soil is seen as part of the healing from colonialism. The land composts their pain into hope. Some of the staff have developed such a sensitivity to the state of the soil that sometimes they only work it when they conclude that the time is right.

“*The land composts their pain into hope*”

The production system is agroforestry where vegetables grow between fruit trees[27]. Their produce helps to tackle the racism of the food system where ‘people of colour disproportionately live in neighbourhoods of food-apartheid[28] and consequently suffer from diet-related illness’.

Leah indicates that beyond the benefits of good nutrition, the first step of the healing process is to grieve. In her book, the shameful list of atrocities suffered by people of colour runs to seven pages[27]. It includes the slave trade, convict leasing, violence from authorities, racial segregation, land theft and contrived difficulties in purchasing land. The net results are inequalities of income, wealth and food access which mean that only <1% of US land is black-owned.

On the farm, healing strategies for releasing pain and attaining personal liberation include connecting with ancestors through prayers and offerings, healing partners and circles, dynamic meditation, community dance and plant medicine. Some even go to the bare soil where anger and frustration can be composted into calm.

The project is a good example of how marginalised soils and human beings can heal together. During the Covid-19 pandemic the farm delivered food to vulnerable families and built raised garden beds for urban households. At the time of writing, the farm enterprise was reaching 10 000 people annually. Many of the faces in photographs of the people touched by the initiatives of the farm show hope – hope for a better future. Naima is building the capacity of the surrounding communities to create more sustainable, resilient and equitable food systems – based around the forgiving, generous soil. This is an approach that could be extended widely to help tackle hunger.

“*This project is a good example of how marginalised soils and human beings can heal together*”

Changing our thinking to help tackle hunger, environmental degradation and heal society

This soil under natural vegetation has rarely been cultivated, but is nevertheless fertile. The soil type is a Stagnic Cambisol that is located near Saint Imier in the Swiss Jura Mountains. The image is © Agroscope (Gabriela Brändle, Urs Zihlmann), LANAT (Andreas Chervet).

Sustainable agricultural production systems can be less productive than intensive agriculture, mainly due to less synthetic fertilisers and pesticides being applied. Although the target for the Sustainable Development Goals is Zero Hunger by 2030, hunger and malnourishment are actually predicted to continue to slowly increase[29]. However, predictions of quantitative scarcity of food from the Food and Agriculture Organization of the United Nations (FAO) have been considered excessive by some scientists[30] because of an underestimation of global food supplies and overestimated demand. Thus agriculture at present produces more than enough food for the current world population. Nevertheless, the nutritional quality of the food in the most vulnerable population groups is likely to deteriorate further because of extra areas where food supply is unreliable due to the adverse health and social and economic impacts of the Covid-19 pandemic.

Even so hunger has its roots deeper than a deficit in food production. **Gilbert Houngbo**, President of the International Fund for Agricultural Development (IFAD), considers that: '**persistent and chronic hunger is the result of poverty, inequality, conflicts, poor government and marginalisation of the most vulnerable**'.

Famine, estimated to affect approximately 41 million people worldwide, is most prevalent in areas of conflict and insecurity and needs to be tackled at the governmental level[31]. The human right of access to adequate food is often hampered by weak political and social interventions to ensure adequate food distribution in poor countries.

Gilbert Houngbo also states that '**the eradication of poverty and hunger requires the development of rural economies**'. These economies are typically sustained by small farms (less than 2 ha) in sub-Saharan Africa and Asia where famines occur and provide 80% of the food production. The farmers need improved policy advice and support in areas such as promoting land rights, risk management for climate change, closing gender gaps in the farming workforce and land owners and

> *“The soil can help us to change if we care to learn from it”*

developing young farmers – all with a view to increasing productivity and sustaining the community[32], and consistent with the broad principles of agroecology[33].

In the higher-yielding areas of Europe and North America, much land is given over to the production of alcoholic drinks and animal feed. If necessary, these can be replaced with cereals and horticulture for direct human consumption. A change of mindset is needed from the many people involved in food production, food distribution and storage and – for all of us consumers – food choice and storage. Such changes will support the healing of the planet as well as society. Everyone is involved. Initiatives such as Community Supported Agriculture where a partnership between farmers and consumers allows the rewards and risks of farming to be shared. This helps to develop the links between soil, agriculture, food and community[34].

Tackling wider environmental problems also needs more than technical approaches. Gus Speth, founder and former president of the World Resources Institute, stated 'I used to think that the top environmental problems were biodiversity loss, ecosystem collapse and climate change. I thought that thirty years of good science could address these problems. I was wrong. The top environmental problems are selfishness, greed and apathy, and to deal with these we need a cultural and spiritual transformation'[35]. Most nations also need deep transformations in order to safeguard human and planetary health. These transformations require a dual focus on curbing excessive affluence and consumption by the rich while avoiding critical human deprivation among the least well off[36].

“The top environmental problems are selfishness, greed and apathy, and to deal with these we need a cultural and spiritual transformation (Speth)”

The soil can help us to change and transform if we care to learn from it. For that to happen we need to become aware of what it can do for us and how it can change our thinking – we need to be open to hear its call on our lives.

The call of the soil and learning from it

This is **Dr Tom Batey**. *I consider Tom to be an underrated star of soil science. He was brought up under tough conditions on a farm in Northumberland. He has written a book about his childhood experiences growing up on the farm in the 1930's and 40's – it is a telling reminder of the importance of family and community, and of working to overcome adversity in what was, by default, a system of sustainable food production*[37]. *He also tells of the relief brought by the coming of the tractor to ease the drudgery of everyday farm work*[37]. *After his dad gave up the farm he trained as an advisor and then majored in soil science consultancy, teaching and research for over 50 years. He has a vast knowledge of soils in farming. I was lucky to be taught by him at the University of Aberdeen. A spade was never far from his hands!*

Humble as the soil itself, Tom sparked my interest in the visual assessment of soil. He suggested that when you hold the soil and observe it, you need to let it tell its story. This related mainly to the colours, the organic matter and the structure. Many years later, I realised that the soil was telling something more compelling, more spiritual. It was calling me and calling all of us to reconnect with it and to learn from it.

Tom and I went to quite a few soil conferences together. On several occasions a senior scientist would speak at a research conference on some new method to describe an aspect of soil biology or soil physics or soil structure measured on samples of soil. When the time for questions came, Tom would stand up, thank the speaker, then ask: What are you trying to find from the sampling and measurements? How does this relate to the body of the soil and its variability? This usually led to some interesting discussions. We all realised that, when sampling and researching the soil, it needs to be considered as an organised whole with the results telling something about the overall function and health of the soil.

I also learned from Tom that farming is husbandry. We are guardians and stewards of the land for those who come after us. This means farming with care and safeguarding for the soil, the crops, fellow workers, the animals and the environment. His earlier book 'Soil Husbandry'[38] focuses on these, as might be expected. Here he presented the six main tenets of good soil husbandry for UK conditions. These are 1. Crop rotations 2. Soil organic matter 3. Field drainage 4. Attention to soil structure 5. Cultivations and 6. Dig and look. Each tenet involves assessing the current condition and then making the most appropriate choice based on the results. For example, in tenet 3, he suggests looking for signs that soil organic matter is approaching a critical low level, such as the presence of weak structure at the soil surface, and, if necessary, taking action – for example by incorporating manure. These principles are relevant to all types of farming, to soil health and, with a bit of imagination, to us. Tenet six is particularly relevant to ourselves. We need to dig and find out more about how the soil functions and then discover what we can learn from these functions.

"We are guardians and stewards of the land for those who come after us"

Soil in a natural system: a steady-state economy

This upland soil is carrying rough pasture that is rarely fertilised yet can support livestock. The soil type is a Dystric Cambisol that is located in Gstaad in Switzerland. The image is © Agroscope (Gabriela Brändle, Urs Zihlmann), LANAT (Andreas Chervet).

Soil doesn't grow – or if it does it grows very slowly. In natural systems the soil operates well as a result of the supply of nutrients from the parent material at a steady, sufficient rate to the plants above. Some soils are naturally richer and more fertile than others. These can support more intensive systems that take more but also give more back as recycling. The nutrients supplied by the organic matter to the system are recycled by the action of the soil biology. Soil in this semi-natural state is very resilient. To me, this combination of steady supply and recycling is a model for a steady state economy that is appropriate for us – an economy of nearly constant size. A steady state economy does not exceed ecological limits by aiming for stable or mildly fluctuating levels in population and steady consumption of energy and materials[39].

Fair distribution of wealth and resources is a critical part of sustaining a steady state economy. Many believe that this is something we need to aim for as a sustainable society in the future. This contrasts with continuous economic growth which involves increased production and consumption of goods and resources in an attempt to supposedly improve our quality of life. The continued pursuit of economic growth is unsustainable due to the overconsumption of natural resources, overproduction of wastes and degradation of the environment – all of which can be seen to compromise national security, particularly of less developed nations. The resources of the earth are finite. Yet initiatives to adopt a steady-state or circular economy continue to be given low priority in most governments and civil societies in the world[40].

If we look to a smaller scale in the soil, the plants and fungi growing in the soil work together to make best use of soil resources.

Roots and fungi: underground co-operation

Mixed media on canvas. Two plant types are shown with root systems that are growing together and are surrounded by fungal strands. The main roots are shown by string, the smaller roots by folded tissue. Soil fungi, here called mycorrhizal fungi, have branching, filamentous strands (shown in white) which penetrate plant roots. The fungi gain energy as sugars from the roots. They form bundled structures inside plant roots (shown as clumps of sawdust) which increase the surface area between roots and fungal strands, improving the supply of nutrients and water to the root in exchange for the energy. In this way the fungal strands can almost double the effectiveness of the root system in gathering nutrients, effectively extending the root system.

This intricate, collaborative network linking individual plants together has been called the Wood Wide Web[41] and is a wonderful example of cooperation in the soil. This system operates in many plants though it is susceptible to damage when disturbed by industrial farming. This underground co-operation is part of the reason for the success of agroforestry and other companion cropping. Much of the co-operation between human beings also occurs unseen and below the surface.

Looking even closer, at the microscopic level, the soil provides living space for the function of a wide biodiversity of microbes.

Soil up close: a network of diversity

Acrylic on board. The boundaries of the soil particles are decorator's filler, the rough surfaces are a mixture of acrylic paint and sawdust and the discs representing bacteria are rapid-set contact adhesive. This image represents a blown-up cross-section of the microscopic structure of the soil in a square of side approximately 0.5 mm. The bounded shapes are soil particles. The areas between the particles represent the soil pores, the voids that hold water or air. The larger pores are air-filled and their surfaces are often coated with a layer of water. The narrower pores are water-filled, shown in blue. The water-filled pores often provide homes for a wide range of bacteria. Bacteria are very numerous and are vital to maintaining the functions of soil, for letting it breathe and cycle nutrients. Up close, the soil is a sub-aquatic wonderland.

The network of porosity in a fertile soil like the one in the painting above, with a wide range of sizes all joined-up, is, to me, like a person who is broad-minded, open-minded and who reaches out to understand where others are coming from and who fosters life and creativity. The different populations of bacteria represented by groups of circles of different colour are exaggerated in size but co-exist very well. This co-existence is successful because they live in distinct families that are linked by the nourishing water and atmosphere in the pores. These pores are arranged to give connection yet allow different life forms to co-exist harmoniously (biodiversity). We can learn that within our society, allowing diverse groups of people of other colours, faiths, gender orientation, sexuality and background to co-exist harmoniously – celebrating our biodiversity – is illustrated by an understanding of soil life.

I find that when I meet someone with different opinions and beliefs to me that the initial antagonism often disappears when I interact with them and take the time to get to know them[42] – connection leading to harmony. Achieving harmony needs an understanding of how our minds work – and the development of the layers of soil give us some clues.

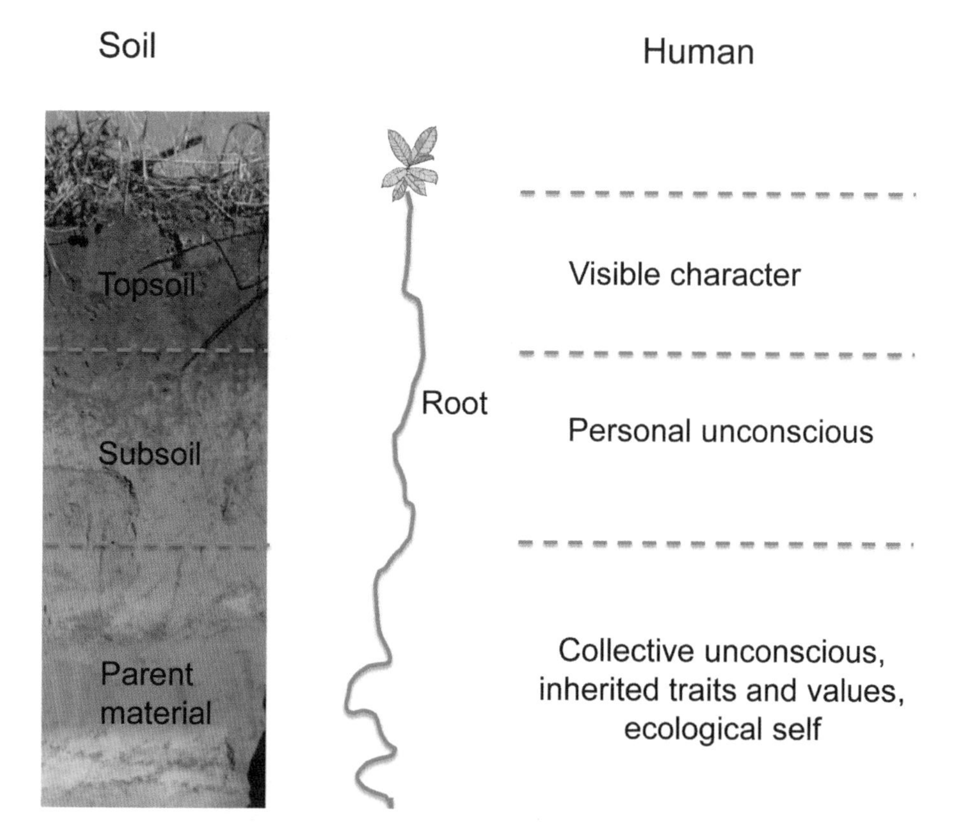

Soil and the workings of the mind

The parallels between layers of human consciousness and the layers of a typical soil are shown above. This likening helps us to understand how our minds work[43]*. At the surface, topsoil represents the visible character or consciousness. The subsoil or second layer is similar to the personal unconscious where hidden potential is stored. Here belong ideas and emotions that influence our actions without our knowledge. The parent material or third layer is the collective unconscious which contains values inherited from our parents and ancestors, that we share with others. This is also the rock of our common humanity, as coined by Gandhi. We need to make more use of what is deep within the soil, and by analogy, what is deep within us. This helps improve mental health by increasing understanding of ourselves and of our connection to others. Touching the soil connects us directly to*

> *it, like when meditation or a similar spiritual practice makes us aware of our collective unconscious as both are peaceful, healing experiences*[43].

This comparison between the soil and the human mind can improve our mental health by bringing an awareness of our interdependence and how mutual support is natural to human beings; this can be accessed readily because we are all connected to each other spiritually. Connecting to what is deep within us also impacts on how we treat others and therefore how we build communities and ultimately society as a whole. By providing mutual support to others, we are tapping into the subsoil and nourishing ourselves.

> *“By providing mutual support to others we are tapping into the subsoil and nourishing ourselves”*

However, many people feel lonely and disconnected to others due to – for example – grief, disagreement, or a past tainted by crime or abuse. I believe that the soil can show an example of how we can recover.

Soil recovery: creative responses to abuse

A crusted soil surface approximately 50cm x 50 cm in area is shown from above; acrylic on canvas. This agricultural soil has been cultivated excessively and sown with cereal seed. However, heavy rainfall caused the soil surface to collapse and, on drying, a crust has formed that protects the soil below. The crop can only weakly grow through the cracks. Thus, the soil protects itself and in doing so prevents good crop growth. This fragmentation of the fertile surface soil has parallels not only with isolation due to abuse but also with our modern individualistic society.

In the above example the soil is usually relatively easily returned to useful productivity by good soil management. The surface is gently loosened with a light cultivator, allowing the other seeds to germinate. Soil thus takes short-term abuse by protecting itself, but readily returns to productivity. This is an example for us of how disagreements are best coped with by taking time before responding so that we can quickly return to our normal selves – an example of non-violent communication[45]. This type of non-cooperative reaction to aggression is similar to the successful use of 'active non-violence' by people opposed to oppressive regimes – such as anti-nuclear movements, resistance to apartheid in South Africa and communist dictatorships in Czechoslovakia and Poland[46].

Naomi Knights coordinates a volunteer befriending project and connects people to reduce social isolation in Midlothian, in the south of Scotland. She matches a volunteer befriender with someone who has been identified as socially isolated – often due to poor mobility or health issues.

As the Covid-19 pandemic took hold, much of connection between people that she facilitated went from face-to-face to telephone or video link. Though communication continued, everyone missed the physical connection both one-to-one and in groups. For some more fortunate people, the Covid lockdowns resembled a fallow period where the soil is not cropped and regains its vitality. The enforced time alone with not much to do provided an opportunity for rest and reflection, leading to a re-assessment of priorities and plans for a fresh approach to life. Nevertheless, for many the increased isolation during lockdown took its toll on mental health.

Naomi perceives that the recovery and preservation of soil is not really solvable by technology but by allowing the work of Nature, a process that involves time and the action of light rain, soil biology and plants. For example, after loosening a crusted soil, the crop may need to be re-seeded and carefully cultivated. The action of rain and the growing crop makes vital connections in the soil porosity – similar to the work of volunteers who help restore communication channels for the slow process of maintaining or re-building mental health.

She considers that restoration of soil resembles recovery from trauma. People who have been hurt will often have created a protective, metaphorical 'shell'. This needs to be gently broken through so they can share their experiences with others in a network that provides emotional support and growth[47]. Critical to this is healing by relating to others either through conversation or through love of shared activities such as cooking, gardening, sport, craft or music. Naomi emphasises that for many people, good mental health is strongly dependent on talking to and relating to people whom we trust – we hold each other safe, and it allows us to thrive.

She believes that, like the resilience given to the soil by the presence of organic matter (humus) that helps to retain nutrients and reduce soil loss by wind and rain, human resilience is strongly helped through connectivity with other people. When people in a community have multiple connections with each other a stronger social fabric is created which is more resilient to disturbances. There was a massive spontaneous neighbourly response at the beginning of Covid-19 and many people looked out for the more vulnerable people in their neighbourhoods. People ran errands, did shopping, walked dogs and spoke at the front door to those who were housebound or isolating. The pandemic has also shown us that we must tackle the several converging crises currently facing us. These are not just the pandemic, but also racial injustice, health and/or income inequalities and climate change. We need to campaign for the rights of key workers and the marginalised who are most affected by these crises. They also need their fair share of resources. It's time for like-minded people to come together and to restore fairness and justice for all.

"It's time for like-minded people to come together and restore fairness and justice for all"

Maybe we can all strengthen our mental health by developing our thinking and world views so that we become resistant to degrading processes such as being stifled by domination (like soil compaction), addicted to consumer goods (like soil contamination) or losing our sense of what is important in life (like soil erosion).

Soil inspired theology: soil and the future

Meet **Rev Dr Terry Biddington**, *Dean of Spiritual Life at the University of Winchester, UK. He runs an annual Soil Day on 'Know your Soil Know your Earth'. He wryly states that his students think he is mad when he brings soil into a theology class. He explores the use of soil processes as models for improving many of our outdated mindsets and for making radical, soil-driven developments in theology.*

He believes that 'the future of all life on the planet depends on our willingness for the soil to once again inform our thought processes. Then we can understand how to live sustainably and interdependently into the future with all other life forms on the planet. We certainly need to grow and nourish the soil so it can feed life. But we need to **think soil** so that we can break through the moribund earth-impoverished layers of our dominant and sterile philosophies and theologies in order to find practical, meaningful, flexible, and nourishing modes of thinking that – informed by awareness of our kinship with the rest of the living world *and* its soils – will lead us towards the more healthy,

> *A soil-inspired theology will allow us to discover a deeper understanding of where we come from, who we really are, and the possibilities for a future in harmony with all other living things*

integrated and sustainable future we all need. From the soil we can emerge into new life.'

His prophetic vision is where 'everything in the soil is part of a generous, co-operative matrix where all life feeds, and is fed by, everything else. How then might a soil-inspired theology change our attitudes to migrant workers, economic migrants, asylum seekers, the unemployed and poor, the marginalised, the disabled and those unable to contribute "economically"? A soil-inspired theology will allow us to discover a deeper understanding of where we come from, who we really are, and the possibilities for a future in harmony with all other living things. For while we have hitherto always found part of our identity by reflecting over centuries on our relationships with other humans, we can only learn more by **deepening our relationship with the soils around us**. This brings forth the future flourishing of all creatures, ourselves included.'[48].

'We must heed the call of the soil' he declares with urgency to his students – and to all of us.

A World of Soil for Healing People and Planet

This is my vision of a soil-inspired society, encompassing Wholeness like the Earth itself. Mixed media on paper. The script was written using dip pen calligraphy.

Degraded soils can be healed by good soil management thereby improving various soil qualities. In a parallel manner, our society can be healed by developing collective life qualities. In the same way that the soil encircles the world, when we develop soil-like properties it helps us to work in unity or Wholeness, holding our world and its people together[49]. A key lesson from soil identified by Terry Biddington is that 'the soil lives because it cooperates and it cooperates to live'.

> “*Like soil we need to come together and work together as an organised whole to create the world we want*”

Like soil we need to come together and work together as an

organised whole to create the world we want. For soil properties and functions to develop, all parts of the soil contribute equally – a model of the fair division of work, inclusive community and the resources needed for a society to work well. Some of the ways we can learn from soil are:

The Worlds of the Soil and the Human

Soil property	Human learning
Aggregates bind particles with roots and fungi and allow the release of plant nutrients, a great hospitality	Understanding and co-operating with others, especially with those who do not share our views, draws us together
Porosity allows creation of networks of interconnection and better living conditions for soil organisms	Showing openness, empathy and compassion to others allows creation of diverse networks and communities
Soil biology is highly interdependent, driving many soil functions at many scales	Living, dynamic connection is fostered by communicating in networks of family, community and nation
No distinct boundaries are present in natural soils where usable resources depend on parent material	A lower consumption lifestyle leads to fairer sharing of resources and inclusive communities
Humus, the soil's hidden essence, grows soil stability, colour and resilience as organic matter is added	Humility, fostered by growth of spirituality*, develops wisdom, an informed conscience and happiness
Greening power, giving life to plants, is fostered by soil fertility, itself related to humus and parent material	Growing healing and spirituality allows access to deep, shared supportive values leading to understanding
Roots allow the soil to be productive, helping to stabilise and keep the integrity of the Earth	Kind words and caring actions by friendly, well-informed people keep the integrity of the Earth
Deepening the topsoil by good management allows roots to spread, increasing humus and greening power	Developing and sharing knowledge and wisdom of individuals promotes community development

**Spirituality is taken here as a deep sense of aliveness and interconnectedness of everything and everyone that drives the emergence of new life.*

Networks of soil-informed people can be seen as part of an overall Wholeness of all people, the environment and our World. Every caring and conserving action, no matter how small, improves the function of that Wholeness. The world of the soil encompasses so much more than providing our food and conserving the environment.

The qualities shown above lead us to paths of healing and hope that involve co-operation, sharing, kindness and compassion. These may seem to be small steps, but as McIntosh[50] states, small solutions are the ones that work, particularly where there is a shared community desire. The response to the recent Covid-19 pandemic showed that this can happen. This needs to be harnessed more to allow the building of alternative institutions and models of the world that permit resistance to oppression, justice and promote human dignity for all[27]. Further, the power of human goodness – like the basic goodness or fertility of the soil – can challenge the powers-that-be that seem ineffective at serving the whole of society equitably. As writer Rutger Bregman[42] states, this hopeful view of human nature is threatening to the powers-that-be – 'a democracy with engaged citizens has no need of career politicians'.

> “ *The qualities (of humanity taken from soil) lead us to paths of healing that involve co-operation, sharing, kindness and compassion* ”

This list looks impressive and, on the face of it, relatively straightforward. But it involves work. We need to take this approach into our homes, offices, schools and politics where McIntosh considers that 'any fool can live in conflict, but it takes guts to live in peace'[51]. In a similar vein, Bregman[42] states that more openness and more humanity are difficult to pursue whereas retaliation, division and tough talk – even dropping bombs – are relatively easy. We need to take heart. Like our soils, human beings are also highly resilient and their ability to develop solutions for seemingly massive problems is much greater than cynics would have us believe[42].

Our ongoing huge challenges include climate change, resource scarcity and dependence on violence to solve disagreements. One of these challenges identified by the Commission for the Human Future[40] is seemingly huge – the national and global failure to understand and act preventatively on global risks to human survival. Let's take that awareness of our problems and act – caring for soils, caring for people and showing compassion. A vision to aim for is that of a World where the Sustainable Development Goals of the United Nations are met[52].

So it's time for action. We need to stop taking our soil for granted, stop over-using it, stop smothering it with more buildings, stop compacting it and neglecting it and start treating it with respect, return resources to it and just get to know it. We stand on it and take it for granted – just as many of those reading this used to take key workers for granted – but Covid-19 changed that.

> *"Let's take that awareness of our problems and act – caring for soils, caring for people and showing compassion"*

The way we take action politically can be inspired by the soil and the tending of plants in a garden. Author and social change activist Sue Goss[53] proposes that we leave behind our current 'mechanical and centralised' government that aims for growth and continual development using its various 'levers' of power and influence. Instead, we need to increase the emphasis on local government that aims to shift our dynamic human eco-system towards a balance that needs monitoring and adjustment – just like gardening. Goss states that this 'garden mind' approach involves creating conditions in which everyone could build their capabilities to thrive, for example a basic income and comprehensive education. She equates these conditions with the provision of rich soil.

My daughter **Cat Ball** strongly believes that we need to work for change by getting to know individuals and seeing their point of view to identify common ground to move forward. A good example of a mechanism to tackle disagreements is provided by Initiatives for Change[54] which focuses on building trust across the World's divides to move to personal change and then to global change. This organisation is committed to transformation of society through changes in human motives and behaviour. Cat also thinks that we need to convince our politicians and policy makers to look beyond the next election or project and think of our long-term responsibilities to our children and grandchildren.

You can deepen your understanding of soil, and ultimately hear its call in your life and to action, by taking the practical and spiritual journey into soil on pages 98–105.

I'll end with a quote from my earlier book[17]: 'Look for beauty that is soil deep. Walk with respect on the Earth and to all its creatures. Look to the small and the simple, look to the beautiful, look below. From there springs health and peace'.

For a healthier future we not only need to conserve our soils, we need to learn from them.

SOIL, MY WORLD

Know me
discover
my worlds
on Earth

Catch from me
the sense
of infinity
within

Touch me
re-member me
to
re-member you

Smell me
the fragrance
of life
and death

Hold me
but not too tight
or I'll slip
away

Break me
make me
gently
without violence

Cover my nakedness
with nature
not cement
nor plastic

Smile at me
as you wipe me
off the floor
into the bin

Learn from me
be inspired
by my generosity
to kindness

Care for me
and in
the future
we'll thrive

To conclude, a practical and a spiritual journey into soil, global change and society

Taking this journey will deepen your understanding of soil and perhaps help you to hear its call in your life.

The journey starts with practical stages of discovery about soil, moves into deeper discovery with some experiments on how soil works and ends with practical actions for mental health and for tackling global change. The spiritual stages of the journey involve meditating or thinking about soil and our connection to it so that we can move towards an increased motivation to act and to inspire others to conserve the soil, the environment and society. The practical activities (on the left of the tables below) and the spiritual activities (on the right of the tables) can be done independently but most are complementary and can be done together.

The activities suggested here and in the spiritual journey are suitable for personal or group use. As stated earlier in the text, spirituality is taken as a deep sense of aliveness and interconnectedness of everything and everyone that drives the emergence of new life.

For the meditational steps, it's best to do a short exercise of breathing and relaxation to enable you to clear your mind and to help inspire your thoughts. There are several examples that you can use. This is a helpful example. First, raise your shoulders towards your ears, hold them and let them go as you relax. Repeat, holding your breath as you raise the shoulders, hold for a second or two, then breathe out as you let them go. Repeat again and become fully aware of how you are.

First steps...

The health of your soil. Your soil could be the soil in your garden or the soil in your local communal park. What would you estimate the health of your soil to be? How do you know this? Take some of your soil in your hand: what does it feel like? Look at it closely: what can you see? How can you tell whether or not it's in a healthy condition? If possible look at soil in different places – under the grass as against that in a vegetable patch or in a flowerbed. Can you spot any differences? If there are, can you tell why?

Begin your spiritual journey. Read the poem 'Soil, my World' on page 97. The poem states 'learn from me'. What can you learn from reading that poem? What would you like to discover on your journey? Do the breathing and relaxation exercise and repeat. What more did you learn after the second reading?

Find the life in your soil and wonder at it. Healthy soil results from having a thriving diversity of life within. A rich biodiversity involves having different creatures living and co-operating together. Tip a handful of soil onto a piece of white paper to see what you can see with the naked eye or a magnifying lens. Then find images of the soil creatures listed on page 10 to check what you've missed! Crumble the soil to make a uniform thin layer over part of the white paper. Look for any small light-coloured particles or creatures. Looking at this surface is like looking at the night sky. Think in wonder how much is hidden and how little we perceive and know about both the soil and the night sky.

Walking the soil I. Find somewhere where you can sit down on the soil in relative isolation to help prevent you from feeling embarrassed by the presence of others. A large garden or a safe, secluded field or wood would be OK. Walk slowly or sit on the soil and feel it give below your feet or damp when you sit down. If you can, find bare soil or soil that is thinly vegetated, especially after rain, and listen to it, smell and watch it. Sitting quietly allows you to become aware of the things that are happening in Nature around you. Think of the roots penetrating deep into the living soil to the parent material. Think of the marvel of this, focus on the feeling of peace and calm brought by being at one with the soil. Bring this peace with you for the rest of the day. This exercise can be simplified by walking slowly across the grass in a park, though it may be less effective.

Discover your soil structure. Take a spade and cut a hole about the width and depth of the spade. This is probably best done in a private garden or well within a local woodland. Take out a slice and place it on the ground or on a table. You can leave it on the spade if necessary. With your fingers loosen it gently while still keeping the slice intact. Your aim is to try to find the structures of the soil – the aggregates. Compare what your soil looks like to the soils shown on the VESS chart at the back of the book. Each row of pictures on the chart shows one kind of structure. Which one of the five is closest to yours?

> **Keeping healthy.** What 'nutrients' do you use to keep your body, mind and spirit in a healthy condition? What does the balance look like between healthy natural nutrients (e.g. organic food and physical exercise) and artificial ones (e.g. processed foods and social media use)?

Find your soil's signature. Take a small handful of soil. Rub it through your fingers with some water so that it feels a bit like thick yogurt. If your soil feels rough and doesn't mould easily in your fingers, it is sandy with coarse particles. If it is easily moulded like plasticine, it is clay with fine particles. If it is in between and feels silky with some grittiness it is probably silt. This simple description of soil particles is called texture. It remains the same no matter how much you work the soil – unless it is heavily eroded. It is determined by the parent material of the soil and is thus part of what makes your soil type unique. What is the texture of your soil? Try measuring the textures of friends' gardens to get an idea of the different types. More detailed descriptions of how to measure soil texture can be found online[1].

> **Parallels between soil and people.** There are many analogies and similarities drawn in this book between what can be said about the soil and what we can say about the character of people. Without referring to the text, check out whether, at this stage of your journey, you can imagine what some of them might be?

Moving on and going deeper……

Discover how soil changes as you go deeper. Take a spade and cut a hole in your garden or earth. Make it a square of spade width and about 30 cm deep if possible. You may need to clean the vertical surfaces with a knife. How does the soil change the deeper down it goes? Can you see different colours and textures? Try to imagine how the soil surfaces might look if you dug down further to sense what lies beneath your feet.

Spiritual Growth. Robyn Travis, who left prison to help keep children off the streets where gang and drug violence was rife, stated that 'sometimes the best messages come from the darkest places'[2]. Seeds need to be covered in soil to absorb moisture and emerge to live from a dark place. In addition, Naomi Knights also states that 'growth happens in the hardest bits of life'. Just as a seed germinates and grows towards the light, we must sometimes take stock, use our internal strength and strive to move into situations where we can flourish. Can you think of times when you have found inspiration or growth from a dark or a hard place?

Discover how soil varies around you and through the season. As you walk through the countryside – or travel through it by train or bus – observe the soil. Look at the variation in colour of different soils. See where the water lies. If you take a regular walk over the same route, try to observe how the same soil varies over time. In the autumn at harvest time look out for healthy soils that have nice rough surfaces and unhealthy ones that have wheel tracks and contain compaction. Can you spot the difference?

The wonder of diversity. Soil has huge biodiversity. How do you encounter life's diversity? Different foods, ideas, or music; people from different cultures, faiths and backgrounds. What does such diversity bring to your community, your personal experience and your spiritual journey?

Find out the effect of compacting the soil. The pores in soil allow it to take in water, air, and other nutrients. Soil porosity ensures healthy soil and enables plants to flourish and to feed life everywhere on the planet. Stand on freshly dug, moist soil for a while. Dig up a few centimetres of the surface where you stood with a trowel and compare to a non-compacted area. Can you see the difference in porosity? Are there other differences?

Moving from fatigue and stress to vitality. Just as unhealthy soil lacks porosity because it has been squashed and deformed, so our bodies, minds and souls can succumb to excessive pressure, stress and fatigue. We need to cultivate our inner porosity! What is it that helps you breathe and feel really alive? How can you work on this aspect of your life?

Letting the soil breathe. Spend some time each week aerating a section of your garden/earth with a fork. Loosen the soil and let it breathe. Watch what happens over time.

Bringing in the new. The equivalent of soil porosity is our ability to be open to what helps us flourish as people. This could involve openness to new experiences, different ideas and cultures and other things that keep us fresh. Make a list of those times when you have experienced such moments of newness in your life.

Spot the carbon being stored in soil. Take a trowel and head off into a nearby wooded area. Look for patches where the soil is covered mostly by leaves rather than vegetation. The leaves contain atmospheric carbon to be stored in the soil. Slice off the top few cm of soil with your trowel and examine how the dead leaves and other vegetation are making a mulch. Dig a bit deeper and see how this layer of mulch makes a transition to the lighter coloured soil below. Sometimes you can see the particles of carbon in this soil.

All life depends on soil. How often do you reflect about your connection with the soil and the fact that all life depends upon it? The Hebrew Scriptures (Genesis 1 and 2) offer an extraordinary insight: humanity comes from the soil. The emphasis is really vivid when seen in the original Hebrew which states that the human 'adam' comes from the earth or 'adamah.' This comparison makes the connection very clear, but how does it change what you feel about the soil or earth and your relationship with it? Try meditating on how the bedrock of soil resembles your deep collective consciousness.

Discover how much water your soil can store. In dry weather extract a lump of soil from the garden and drop it into a bucket half-filled with water. The water level should drop as the soil takes up the water. If the soil disperses in the water it shows low stability and water uptake will be low.

Benevolence. Satish Kumar, peace and environment activist, Schumacher College, thinks that we need to create a movement of 'benevolence and non-violence, for example, by argument and by practical action'[3]. He considers that the benevolence of the soil is endless. How can we tap into that benevolence to bring about such a movement?

Progressing to actions……

Check out your diet. Can you choose a soil-friendly diet? Although organic food may seem an obvious choice, smaller, local businesses may be better than larger organisations as they are likely to operate at a smaller scale and be more hands-on. Organic is not essential though, products from animals that lived outdoors are usually good. Find out where your food comes from. Go to a farmer's market or an agricultural show. Chat to stall holders where there's food you would like to buy – ask them about their soils and what grows best in which soil. Ask how important soil conditions are for the quality of their food.

> **Organic farming and health.** Organic farming is the most commonly known agroecological farming system. The four guiding principles of organic farming have been listed as health, fairness, ecological balance and care[4]. Think about all the ways that organic farming helps planetary health, animal health and human health. How can you bring these thoughts to others?

Try agroecology in the garden. Maintain fertility using composts and cover crops. Minimise soil disturbance by using no-till gardening[5]. Whatever system you use, control weeds manually and only if you need to. Best of all, sit and admire the flowers while eating the veggies!

> **The call to care.** Soil is shown to be basically good, like human beings. Think how it cares for us and shows us how to extend that care to others. Focusing on others can help lead to peace. 'Peace comes from within. Do not seek it without'. How does the soil inform the achievement of such peace? The Jain Guru considers that 'The purpose of your learning and of your living and all other endeavour is to attain a state of equilibrium and harmony'. Do you agree? How can the soil help us to attain this?

Try living in a steady-state economy. The soil is a great example of a co-operative steady state system, that works well together and is heavily dependent on recycling and cooperation with other organisms for nutrition. Inputs of food and fuel from outside are minimal. Try copying this approach for a while – you may need to buy in some basic supplies first!

Motivating climate change action. People get very concerned about those who either dismiss climate change or take token attempts to mitigate it. The soil helps climate change by the functions of storing carbon and water and conserving nutrients that would otherwise cause pollution. Meditate on these functions – think of conserving and enhancing these and their effects on crops, plants and human beings. Tackling climate change is notorious for words and not action. Naomi Klein states 'But we need to be very clear: because of our decades of collective denial, no gradual incremental options are now available to us'[6]. Can you think of any actions on climate change that might spring up like growth from the soil? This is an important subject for identifying common ground with others to become 'engaged citizens'.

Describing a healthy soil. You started this journey by trying to find a healthy soil. Take some of the healthiest soil that you found in your hand. Look at it closely, feel it cool on your hand and (if it's from a field or garden) supportive under your feet. From what you have learned on this journey, can you identify what makes this soil healthy? Key properties are connected porosity, moist but not wet or dry, dark with organic matter, strands of fungus, roots and the presence of mites and worms – signs of fertility and greening power. Hold these properties in your mind and look for them in other soils that you encounter in the future.

Walking the soil II. You're coming towards the end of your journey. As in the earlier 'Walking the soil' exercise, find somewhere where you can sit down on the soil in relative isolation to help prevent you from feeling embarrassed by others. A large garden or a safe, secluded field or wood would be OK. Walk slowly or sit on the soil and feel it give below your feet or damp when you sit down. Think of your roots extending below the grass roots of popular culture and populism to your parent material, your core values that you share with others. Think of how the soil resembles your unity and connection with others and try to express compassion and love for others, the soil and all of Nature. This brings peace. Try to remember this in the next few days. This exercise can be simplified by walking slowly across the grass in a park, though it may be less effective.

Help others to connect with soil. Help others, particularly children, to feel connected to the soil. Talk about the soil in the school or home garden and link it to the production of food. Resources are available in the 'Soils for young people' section in Further Reading. Meet up with others to fly the flag for soil – join social media groups and share with environmental groups, community garden groups, farmers and politicians.

Bringing the vision 'World of Soil' to reality. Refer to the picture and table of the World of Soil on pages 92–93. Can you develop your own vision of a soil-inspired society? What would be your priorities? What would your world look like? One hint is to consider how everything that you do and everything that you consume can help conserve the resources of Nature – and of soil. Can you share it with someone – providing the rich soil for others to thrive with you? How would you start to bring it into being? To help you to achieve change, try the iListen (a quiet time of reflection) offered on the Initiatives for Change website[7].

The end for now……though it's just the beginning. Try to use these insights and knowledge daily and take them to family and friends.

ACKNOWLEDGEMENTS

Mr Tom Henry, artist and teacher, helped me to transform my vague ideas on illustrating the soil into real artworks. He contributed ideas, mock-ups, techniques, materials and laughs along the way. This book has been greatly enriched by the contributions of colleagues who helped me through my career. These include soils specialists who are leaders in their research areas: the late Dr Brennan Soane, Dr Joanna Cloy, Dr Paul Hargreaves, Professor Bryan Griffiths and Dr Rachel Guimarães. A mischievous lover of rhyme, Dr Paul Hargreaves wrote the haiku and also helped with editing.

This book contains the fruits of much of my life's work into research, on consultancy and in teaching on soil. I am grateful to the many other colleagues, at home and abroad, who supported me along the way. Thanks also to the funders of my activities, the Scottish Office, the Scottish Government, the UK Research Councils, the European Union and the Universities of Paraná and São Paolo, Brazil and Lincoln University, New Zealand. Thanks to those postgraduate and postdoctoral students and researchers who sought me out, often with funding. These include Rachel Guimarães (Brazil), the late Alvaro DaSilva (Brazil), Mansonia Pulido Moncada (Venezuela), Mary Norton Scherbatskoy (USA), Hiroko Akiyama (Japan), Ignaçio Mariscal (Spain), Mandy Liesch (USA), Rattan Lal (USA), Keith Cameron (New Zealand), Lars Munkholm (Denmark), Per Schjønning (Denmark), Lothar Mueller (Germany), Friedrich Tebrügge (Germany), Sissel Hansen (Norway), Bishal Sitaula (Norway), Laurent Bruckler (France), G. Monnier (France), Josephine Peigné (France), and Cássio Tormena (Brazil). Thanks to Willie Towers and Willie Donald for encouragement and suggestions.

I am grateful to the farmers for keeping me grounded in reality with their contributions: Brian Muirden, Douglas Christie, Mary Norton Scherbatskoy and Naima Penniman. Theologian Rev Dr Terry Biddington came to me looking for advice and soon found himself making a substantial addition to the text, including suggesting and contributing to the practical and spiritual journey into soil. This was a lucky encounter as was that with Naomi Knights. I joined her band of community volunteers and she was soon spending hours discussing the text, illustrations and artwork and soil in general over Zoom and the telephone.

A special thankyou to Dr Tom Batey who started off teaching me soil management at the University of Aberdeen almost 50 years ago and has provided consistent tremendous support ever since. To me he is the doyen of soils specialists and agriculturalists and his contribution (heavily edited by me) hopefully reveals this. Thanks also to my sister for her thoughts on her lovely garden. I am grateful to my daughter for introducing the book, for her ideas on progressive politics and for her patient editing of the text – again and again. Finally, thanks to my wife for posing with her hands for several pictures and for invaluable advice with the artwork and the writing. This book has been a long time coming, partly because of the time needed to create the artworks. Thus, although it might have been appropriate for her to do otherwise as I sat for hours in front of a laptop, my wife provided much valuable encouragement and was a great springboard for ideas.

Nick Hayward provided the portraits for the Foreword and on the back cover. For permission to reproduce photographs, the publisher gratefully acknowledges: Dr Marinus Brouwers, Clapiers, France for the figure on page 20, Dr Gabriela Brändle, Agroscope, Zurich, Switzerland for the figures on pages 27, 74 and 79, Dr Urs Zihlman for the soils information on pages 74 and 79, 'No-till farmer' for the figure on page 41, and Dr Xavier Poux for the graphic on page 61. The figures on page 71 are courtesy of Soul Fire Farm, Vermont with the upper and lower images by Naima Penniman and the middle image by Neshima-Vitale Penniman.

GLOSSARY

These terms are explained in greater detail in the text

Aggregate	A gathering of soil particles stuck together by soil organic matter and clay that is porous and that forms the basic building blocks of soil.
Agroecology	Sustainable farming systems that work with Nature. These include organic farming, regenerative agriculture and low-input conservation agriculture, among others.
Agroforestry	Agriculture where trees and crops are grown together on the same land
Compaction	Soil degradation where soil particles are squashed together by machinery reducing the porosity between them
Companion crop	A crop sown with another crop to improve yield or crop protection from pests
Conservation tillage	Minimised frequency and intensity of tillage to give economic and environmental benefits
Erosion	Soil degradation where soil is detached and carried away by the action of wind or running water.
Greening power	The ability of the soil to cause seed germination and to grow something green
Mob grazing	Grazing of a large number of animals over short periods to mimic natural grazing
No-tillage	A conservation tillage practice where seeds are sown directly into soil not tilled since the previous crop
Parent material	The parent material is the foundation of rock or deposit from which the soil is formed. It is similar to our deep unconscious mind

	which contains values inherited from our parents and ancestors.
Permaculture	An agricultural system which attempts to integrate human activity with natural surroundings to create efficient self-sufficient ecosystems
Soil health	The ability of the soil to function and to sustain plants, animals and human beings.
Soil pore connectivity	The extent of linkage of soil pores to create porosity that absorbs and conducts moisture and allows oxygen to reach soil organisms
Soil porosity	The fraction of the total volume of soil that is taken up by the voids between soil particles and is occupied by either air or water
Soil organic matter	The organic component of soil consisting of plant and animal and microbial residues in a range of states of decomposition
Soil structure	A summary description of the sizes and porosities of the aggregates and porosity that make up the soil.
Soil texture	A summary description of the proportions of soil particles that are sand, silt or clay
VESS	Visual Evaluation of Soil Structure. A score of soil health based on the quality of the soil structure. It is estimated from a spadeful of soil using simple instructions and a visual key https://www.sruc.ac.uk/business-services/sac-consulting/agricultural-production/soils/soil-health-testing/

NOTES

Part I. Healthy Soil

[1.] Molloy, L. 1998. *Soils in the New Zealand landscape: the living mantle.* 2nd Edition. New Zealand Society of Soil Science, Canterbury, New Zealand.
[2.] https://www.soilfoodweb.com/about/
[3.] Brevik, E.C., Slaughter, L., Singh, B.R., Steffan, J.J., Collier, D., Barnhart, P. and Pereira, P. 2020. Soil and human health: current status and future needs. Air, Soil and Water Research 13: 1–23.
[4.] Sweet, V. 2018. *Slow medicine: the way to healing.* Riverhead Books, New York, USA.
[5.] Maddocks, F. 2013. *Hildegard of Bingen: the woman of her age.* Faber and Faber, London, UK.
[6.] Lovelock, J. 1979. *Gaia: a new look at life on Earth.* Oxford University Press, Oxford, UK.
[7.] Philippot, L., Griffiths, B.S. and Langenheder, S. 2021. Microbial community resilience across ecosystems and multiple disturbances. Microbiology and Molecular Biology Reviews 85 (2) https://doi.org/10.1128/mmbr.00026-20
[8.] Ball, B.C., Hargreaves, P.R. and Watson, C.A. 2018. A framework of connections between soil and people can help improve sustainability of the food system and soil functions. Ambio 47: 269–283.
[9.] Lal, R. 2009. Soils and world food security. Soil & Tillage Research 102: 1–4.
[10.] Ohlson, K. 2014. *The soil will save us: how scientists, farmers and foodies are healing the soil to save the planet.* Rodale, New York, USA.
[11.] IPBES, 2019. *The global assessment report on Biodiversity and Ecosystem Services.* Summary for Policymakers. Intergovernmental Science-Policy Platform on Biodiversity and Ecosystem Services, Bonn, Germany.
[12.] Ball, B.C. 2013. Soil structure and greenhouse gas emissions: a synthesis of 20 years of experimentation. European Journal of Soil Science 64: 357–373.
[13.] Houser, M. and Stuart, D. 2019. An accelerating treadmill and an

overlooked contradiction in industrial agriculture: Climate change and nitrogen fertilizer. Journal of Agrarian Change 20: 215–237.
[14] Guimarães, R M. L, Neves, A.F., Silva, W.G., Rogers, C.D., Ball, B.C., Montes, C.R. and Pereira, B.F. 2017. The merits of the Visual Evaluation of Soil Structure method (VESS) for assessing soil physical quality in the remote, undeveloped regions of the Amazon basin. Soil & Tillage Research 173: 75–82 http://dx.doi.org/10.1016/j.still.2016.10.014
[15] Ball, B.C., Batey, T. and Munkholm, L. 2007. Field assessment of soil structural quality – a development of the Peerlkamp test. Soil Use and Management 23: 329–337.
[16] Klaus, G. 2015. *Soil – a precious natural resource.* Publisher National Research Programme, Federal Office for the Environment, Federal Office for Agriculture and Federal Office for Spatial Development, Switzerland. Available (in 2021) at https://www.mnsoilscientist.org/soil.PDF
[17] Wall, D.H., Nielsen, U.N. and Six, J. 2015. Soil biodiversity and human health. Nature 528: 69–76.
[18] Howard, A. 1947. *The soil and health: a study of organic agriculture.* The Devin-Adair Company, New York, USA.

Part II. Healthy Planet

[1] Crippa, M., Solazzo, E., Guizzardi, D., Monforti-Ferrario, F., Tubiello, F.N. and Leip, A. 2021. Food systems are responsible for a third of global anthropogenic GHG emissions. Nature Food 2: 198–209.
[2] EAT-Lancet Commission Brief for Farmers, 2019 https://eatforum.org/lancet-commission/farmers/
[3] National Food Strategy, 2021 Part 2 The Plan (UK) https://www.nationalfoodstrategy.org/the-report/
[4] Monbiot, G. 2022. *Regenesis: feeding the world without devouring the planet.* Penguin, London, UK.
[5] Tudge, C. 2003. *So shall we reap – what's gone wrong with the world's food and how to fix it.* Penguin, London, UK.
[6] Holt-Giménez, E., Shattuck, A., Altieri, M., Herren, H. and Gliessen, S. 2012. We already grow enough food for 12 million people…and still can't end hunger. Journal of Sustainable Agriculture 36: 595–598.
[7] Surviving and thriving in the 21st Century, Commission for the Human

Future, 2020 https://humanfuture.net/sites/default/files/CHF_Roundtable_Report_March_2020.pdf
The ten global catastrophic risks identified were, in no particular order: 1. decline of natural resources, particularly water 2. collapse of ecosystems and loss of biodiversity 3. human population growth beyond Earth's carrying capacity 4. global warming and human-induced climate change 5. chemical pollution of the Earth system, including the atmosphere and oceans 6. rising food insecurity and failing nutritional quality 7. nuclear weapons and other weapons of mass destruction 8. pandemics of new and untreatable disease 9. the advent of powerful, uncontrolled new technology and 10. national and global failure to understand and act preventatively on these risks.

[8.] Pierzynski, G.M. Soil: earth's largest natural water filter. Kansas State University, USA. https://www.wqpmag.com/soil-earths-largest-natural-water-filter

[9.] A croft is a small unit of agricultural land which often, but not always, contains a house. The person who lives on the croft is called a crofter.

[10.] Srivastava, P., Kumar, A., Behera, S.K., Sharma, Y.K and Singh, N. 2012. Soil carbon sequestration: an innovative strategy for reducing atmospheric carbon dioxide concentration. Biodiversity and Conservation 21: 1343–1358.

[11.] Sharma, L.K. and Bali, S.K. 2018. A review of methods to improve nitrogen use efficiency in agriculture. Sustainability 10: 51.

[12.] Ball, B.C. 2013. Soil structure and greenhouse gas emissions: a synthesis of 20 years of experimentation. European Journal of Soil Science 64: 357–373.

[13.] Dunne, D. 2020. Nitrogen fertiliser use could 'threaten global climate goals'. https://www.carbonbrief.org/nitrogen-fertiliser-use-could-threaten-global-climate-goals

[14.] Gade, A.L., Hauschild, M.Z. and Laurent, A. 2021. Globally differentiated effect factors for characterising terrestrial acidification in life cycle impact assessment. Science of the Total Environment 761, 143280.

[15.] Lal, R. 2009. Soils and world food security. Soil & Tillage Research 102: 1–4.

[16.] Weis, T. 2010. The accelerating biophysical contradictions of industrial capitalist agriculture. Journal of Agrarian Change 10: 315–341.

[17.] Kummu, M., Heino, M., Taka, M., Varis, O. and Viviroli, D. 2021.

Climate change risks pushing one-third of global food production outside the safe climatic space. One Earth 4: 720–729.

[18.] Poore, J. and Nemecek, T. 2018. Reducing food's environmental impacts through producers and consumers. Science 360, 6392: 987–992.

[19.] Nitrogen in Europe: Current problems and future solutions 2009. The Barsac Declaration: Environmental Sustainability and the Demitarian Diet. http://www.nine-esf.org/node/280/index.html

[20.] Bullock, J.M., Dhanjal-Adams, K.L., Milne, A., Oliver, T.H., Todman, L.C., Whitmore, A.P. and Pywell, R.F. 2017. Resilience and food security: rethinking an agricultural concept. Journal of Ecology 105: 880–884.

[21.] Thomas, E., Prabha, V.S., Kurien, V.T. and Thomas, A.P. 2020. The potential of earthworms in soil carbon storage: a review. Environmental and Experimental Biology 18: 61–75.

[22.] Lal, R. 2013. Principles of soil management. In: Lal, R. and Stewart, B.A. (eds) *Principles of Sustainable Soil Management in Agroecosystems.* Advances in Soil Science book series, CRC Press, Taylor and Francis Group, Boca Raton, FL, USA, 1–18.

[23.] IPES-Food, 2016. *From uniformity to diversity: A paradigm shift from industrial agriculture to diversified agroecological systems.* International Panel of Experts on Sustainable Food Systems.

[24.] Poux, X. and Aubert, P.-M. 2018. An agroecological Europe in 2050: multifunctional agriculture for healthy eating. Findings from the Ten Years for Agroecology (TYFA) modelling exercise, IDDRI-AScA, *Study* N°09/18.

[25.] Why regenerative agriculture? Regeneration International https://regenerationinternational.org/why-regenerative-agriculture/ With its emphasis on practices such as conservation tillage, cover cropping, holistic grazing and minimal chemical inputs, regenerative agriculture is popular with farmers. However there needs to be careful consideration of the context of the practices to be promoted otherwise their benefits may not appear (see Giller, K.E., Hijbeek, R., Andersson, J.A. and Sumberg, J. 2021. Regenerative agriculture: an agronomic perspective. Outlook on Agriculture 50: 13–25).

[26.] What is conservation agriculture? European Conservation Agriculture Federation https://www.agricology.co.uk/resources/what-conservation-agriculture

[27.] Climate-smart agriculture, Food and Agriculture Organisation of the

United Nations http://www.fao.org/climate-smart-agriculture/en/

28. Altieri, M.A., Nicholls, C.I., Henao, A. et al. 2015. Agroecology and the design of climate change-resilient farming systems. Agronomy for Sustainable Development 35: 869–890.

29. Montgomery, D.R. 2017. *Growing a revolution: bringing our soil back to life.* Norton, New York.

30. Lal, R., Bouma, J., Brevik, E., Dawson, L., Field, D.J., Glaser, B., Hatano, R., Hartemink, A. et al. 2021. Soils and sustainable development goals of the United Nations (New York, USA): an IUSS perspective. Geoderma Regional 25: e00398.

31. Soane, B.D., Ball, B.C., Arvidsson, J., Basch, G., Moreno, F. and Roger-Estrade, J. 2012. No-till in northern, western and south-western Europe: a review of problems and opportunities for crop production and the environment. Soil and Tillage Research 118: 66–87.

32. O'Sullivan, M.F. 1985. Water redistribution and use by barley in two ploughed and direct drilled stagnogley soils. Journal of agricultural Engineering Research 31:171–184.

33. Bane, P. 2012. *The permaculture handbook.* New Society, Canada.

34. Schjønning, P., Elmholt, S., Munkholm, L.J. and Debosz, K. 2002. Soil quality aspects of humid sandy loams as influenced by organic and conventional long-term management. Agriculture, Ecosystems and Environment 88: 195–214.

35. Reeve, J.R., Hoagland, L.A., Villalba, J.J., Carr, P.M., Atucha, A., Cambardella, C., Davis, D.R. and Delate, K. 2016. Organic farming, soil health and food quality: considering possible links. Advances in Agronomy 137: 319–367.

36. Brevik, E.C., Slaughter, L., Singh, B.R., Steffan, J.J., Collier, D., Barnhart, P. and Pereira, P. 2020. Soil and human health: current status and future needs. Air, Soil and Water Research 13: 1–23.

37. Penniman, L. 2018. *Farming while black: Soul Fire Farm's practical guide to liberation on the land.* Chelsea Green, Vermont, USA.

38. Howard, A. 1947. *The soil and health: a study of organic agriculture.* The Devin-Adair Company, New York, USA.

39. The healing power of soil, Centre for Sustaining Agriculture and Natural Resources, Washington State University, USA https://csanr.wsu.edu/the-healing-power-of-soil/

[40.] Shepherd, T.G. 2009. *Visual soil assessment. Vol. 1. Field guide for pastoral grazing and cropping on flat rolling country,* 2nd Edition. Palmerston North, New Zealand: Horizons Regional Council.
[41.] Cameron, L., Chagunda, M.G.G., Roberts, D.J. and Lee, M.A. 2018. A comparison of milk yields and methane production from three contrasting high-yielding dairy cattle feeding regimes: cut-and-carry, partial grazing and total mixed ration. Grass and Forage Science 75: 789–797.
[42.] Byrnes, R.C., Eastburn, D.J., Tate, K.W. and Roche, L.M. 2018. A global meta-analysis of grazing impacts on soil health indicators. Journal of Environmental Quality 47: 758–765.
[43.] Hargreaves, P.R., Baker, K.L., Graceson, A., Bonnett, S.A.F., Ball, B.C. and Cloy, J.M. 2021. Use of nitrification inhibitor reduces nitrous oxide (N_2O) emissions from compacted grassland with different soil textures and climatic conditions. Agriculture, Ecosystems & Environment 310:107307.
[44.] Savory, A. and Butterfield, J. 2016. Holistic management: a commonsense revolution to restore our environment. Island Press, Washington, USA.
[45.] The '4 per 1000 initiative' on building carbon stocks in soil to contribute to reducing the carbon dioxide concentration in the Earth's atmosphere, CGIAR, France https://www.4p1000.org/
[46.] Griscom, B.W., Adams, J., Ellis, P.W., Houghton, R.A., Lomax, G., Miteva, G.A. et al. 2017. Natural climate solutions. PNAS 114: 11645–11650.
[47.] Pulido-Moncada, M., Ball, B.C. and Cornelis, W. 2021. Advances in visual techniques to measure soil structure. In: Otten, W. (Editor) *Advances in measuring soil health.* pp. 71–110 Burleigh Dodds, Cambridge, UK.
[48.] Rebanks, J. 2020. *English pastoral: an inheritance.* Allen Lane/Penguin, UK.
[49.] Ball, B.C. 2015. *The landscape below: soil, soul and agriculture.* Wild Goose, Glasgow.
[50.] Gordon, A.M., Newman, S. M. and Coleman, B.R.W. 2018. *Temperate agroforestry systems* (2nd edition). CABI, Wallingford, UK.
[51.] Intercropping and companion planting, Ecosystems United https://ecosystemsunited.com/2019/03/05/the-difference-between-intercropping-and-companion-planting/
[52.] Morrison, J. 2016. The 'Great Green Wall' didn't stop desertification, but it evolved into something that might. Smithsonian Magazine August 23, 2016.
[53.] Woodland Crofts http://woodlandcrofts.org/

[54.] Scherbatskoy, M. 2021. *My Land: an agricultural journey.* Available from Ceann nah-Àirigh, Grimsay, North Uist, HS6 5DA, UK.
[55.] Blythman, J. A breath of fresh air in the debate about meat and carbon, The Grocer, June 2021 https://www.thegrocer.co.uk/health/a-breath-of-fresh-air-in-the-debate-about-meat-and-carbon/657296.article
[56.] Pullman, N. A new model for farming? June 2020 https://wickedleeks.riverford.co.uk/features/farming-climate-change-health-biodiversity/new-model-farming
[57.] Neuhoff, D. and Kwesiga, J. 2021. Para-organic intensification of future farming as alternative concept to reactor-based staple food production in Africa. Organic Agriculture 11: 209–215.
[58.] Jones, D.L., Cross, P., Withers, P.J.A., DeLuca, T.H., Robinson, D.A., Quilliam, R.S., Harris, I.M., Chadwick, D.R. et al. 2013. Nutrient stripping: the global disparity between food security and soil nutrient stocks. Journal of Applied Ecology 50: 851–862.
[59.] Ball, B.C., Hargreaves, P.R. and Watson, C.A. 2018. A framework of connections between soil and people can help improve sustainability of the food system and soil functions. Ambio 47: 269–283.
[60.] Gliessman, S. 2013. Agroecology: growing the roots of resistance. Agroecology and Sustainable Food Systems 37: 19–31.

Part III. Healthy Lives

[1.] National Food Strategy, 2021 Part 2 The Plan (UK) https://www.nationalfoodstrategy.org/the-report/
[2.] Oliver, M.A. and Gregory, P.J. 2015. Soil, food security and human health: a review. European Journal of Soil Science 66, 257–276.
[3.] Lal, R. (editor) 2021. *The soil-human health-nexus.* CRC Press, Boca Raton, USA.
[4.] Ottman, N., Ruokolainen, L., Suomalainen, A., Sinkko, H., Karisola, P., Lehtimäki, J., Lehto, M., Hanski, I., Alenius, H. and Fyhrquist, N. 2019. Soil exposure modifies the gut microbiota and support immune tolerance in a mouse model. Journal of Allergy and Clinical Immunology 143: 1198–1206.
[5.] Macciochi, J. Ask the scientist: here's what to do to boost your immune system. The Times, March 2020 https://www.thetimes.co.uk/article/ask-

the-scientist-heres-what-to-do-to-boost-your-immune-system-lzwxtdhz6

[6.] Núñez-Delgado, A. 2020. SARS-CoV-2 in soils. Environmental Research 190: 11045.

[7.] Brevik, E.C., Slaughter, L., Singh, B.R., Steffan, J.J., Collier, D., Barnhart, P. and Pereira, P. 2020. Soil and human health: current status and future needs. Air, Soil and Water Research 13: 1–23.

[8.] Soil-transmitted helminthiases, World Health Organisation https://www.who.int/health-topics/soil-transmitted-helminthiases#tab=tab_1

[9.] Katz, B.G. 2020. Exploring the widespread impacts of ongoing nitrogen pollution. Eos 101, https://doi.org/10.1029/2020EO149413

[10.] Bittman. S., Brook, J., Bleeker, A. and Bruulsema, T. 2014. Air quality, health effects and management of ammonia emissions from fertilisers. In: Taylor, E. and McMillan, A. (eds). Air Quality Management. Springer, Dordrecht.

[11.] Whole Health Agriculture: Linking farming, food and health, England and Wales https://wholehealthag.org/about/manifesto/

[12.] Jones, D.L., Cross, P., Withers, P.J.A., DeLuca, T.H., Robinson, D.A., Quilliam, R.S., Harris, I.M., Chadwick, D.R. et al. 2013. Nutrient stripping: the global disparity between food security and soil nutrient stocks. Journal of Applied Ecology 50: 851–862.

[13.] Pesticide residues in food, World Health Organisation, 2018 https://www.who.int/news-room/fact-sheets/detail/pesticide-residues-in-food

[14.] Don't let the fear of pesticides stop you from eating fruit and veggies, Healthline Media, 2021 https://www.healthline.com/health-news/dont-let-a-fear-of-pesticides-stop-you-from-eating-fruits-and-veggies

[15.] Pesticide Action Network Europe, Brussels https://www.pan-europe.info/about-us/what-we-do

[16.] Manyi-Loh, C., Mamphweli, S., Meyer, E. and Okoh, A. 2018. Antibiotic use in agriculture and its consequential resistance in environmental sources: potential public health implications. Molecules 23: 795.

[17.] Ball, B.C. 2015. *The landscape below: soil, soul and agriculture.* Wild Goose, Glasgow, introduction.

[18.] Taylor, B.B. 2011. *An altar in the world: finding the sacred beneath our feet.* Canterbury Press, Norwich, UK.

[19.] Oschman, J.L., Chevalier, G. and Brown, R. 2015. The effects of grounding (earthing) on inflammation, the immune response, wound healing, and prevention and treatment of chronic inflammatory and autoimmune diseases. Journal of Inflammation Research 8: 83–96.

[20]. In brief: Tai Chi gives immune system a boost, Harvard Health Publishing, 2010. https://www.health.harvard.edu/newsletter_article/in-brief-tai-chi-gives-immune-system-a-boost

[21]. Lowry, C.A., Hollis, J.H., de Vries, A., Pan, B., Brunet, L.R., Hunt, J.R.F. et al. 2007. Identification of an immune-responsive mesolimbocortical serotonergic system: potential role in regulation of emotional behavior. Neuroscience 146: 756–772.

[22]. Chalmin-Piu, L.S., Griffiths, A., Roe, J., Heaton, T. and Cameron, R. 2021. Why garden? – Attitudes and the perceived health benefits of home gardening, Cities 112: 103118.

[23]. Wakefield, S., Yeudall, F., Taron, C., Reynolds, J. and Skinner, A. 2007. *Growing urban health: Community gardening in East Toronto.* Health Promotion International 22: 92–101.

[24]. Paul, J. 2013. 'Please pick me': how Incredible Edible Todmorden is repurposing the commons for open source food and agricultural biodiversity. In: Franzo, J., Hunter, D., Borelli, T. and Mattei, F. (eds.). *Diversifying Foods and Diets: Using Agricultural Biodiversity to Improve Nutrition and Health,* pp. 336–345. Earthscan, Routledge, Oxford, UK.

[25]. Therapeutic Gardening, Trellis Scotland, Perth https://www.trellisscotland.org.uk/content/therapeutic-gardening

[26]. Walker, J. 2016. *Weeds: an organic, earth-friendly guide to their identification, use and control.* Earth-friendly Books, UK.

[27]. Penniman, L. 2018. *Farming while black: Soul Fire Farm's practical guide to liberation on the land.* Chelsea Green, Vermont, USA.

[28]. Food apartheid is where there is restricted access to healthy, affordable food for low income communities.

[29]. FAO, IFAD, UNICEF, WFP and WHO. 2020. *The state of food security and nutrition in the world 2020.* Transforming food systems for affordable healthy diets. Rome, FAO.

[30]. Kassam, A. and Kassam, L. 2020. *Re-thinking food and agriculture.* Woodhead Publishing, Elsevier, UK.

[31]. Famine alert: how WFP is tackling this other deadly pandemic. World Food Programme, Italy https://www.wfp.org/stories/famine-hunger-un-world-food-programme-united-nations

[32.] Fan, S. and Rue, C. 2020. The role of smallholder farms in a changing world. In: Gomez y Paloma, S., Riesgo, L. and Louhichi, K. (eds). *The role of smallholder farms in food and nutrition security.* Springer, Cham., pp. 13–28.
[33.] Gliessman, S. 2013. Agroecology: growing the roots of resistance. Agroecology and Sustainable Food Systems 37: 19–31.
[34.] Community Supported Agriculture 2022. https://communitysupportedagriculture.org.uk/
[35.] Speth, G. A new consciousness and the eight-fold way towards sustainability. https://earthcharter.org/podcasts/gus-speth/?gclid=Cj0KCQiA4b2MBhD2ARIsAIrcB-R4bgLox81TEnYlvQ1ihbTrcN8djxEOT92S0ogHP5qTuNmeKltelxQaAnPfEALw_wcB Costa Rica.
[36.] Fanning, A.L., O'Neill, D.W., Hickel, J. and Roux, N. 2021. The social shortfall and ecological overshoot of nations. Nature Sustainability https://doi.org/10.1038/s41893-021-00799-z
[37.] Batey, T. 2020. *A country bairn: experiences of life and work on a family farm 1933–1959.* The Heritage Centre, Bellingham, Northumbria, UK.
[38.] Batey, T. 1988. *Soil Husbandry: a practical guide to the use and management of soils.* Published by the author.
[39.] Dietz, R. and O'Neill, D. 2013. *Enough is enough: building a sustainable economy in a world of finite resources.* Earthscan/Routledge, Abingdon, UK.
[40.] Surviving and thriving in the 21st Century, Commission for the Human Future, 2020 https://humanfuture.net/sites/default/files/CHF_Roundtable_Report_March_2020.pdf
[41.] Sheldrake, M. 2020. *Entangled life: how fungi make our worlds, change our minds and shape our futures.* Bodley Head, London.
[42.] Bregman, R. 2020. *Humankind: a hopeful history.* Bloomsbury, London, UK.
[43.] Ball, B.C., Hargreaves, P.R. and Watson, C.A. 2018. A framework of connections between soil and people can help improve sustainability of the food system and soil functions. Ambio 47: 269–283.
[44.] Ball, B.C. 2013. Spiritual aspects of sustainable soil management. In: Lal, R. and Stewart, B.A. (eds) *Principles of Sustainable Soil Management in Agroecosystems.* Advances in Soil Science book series, CRC Press, Taylor and Francis Group, Boca Raton, FL, USA, 257–284.
[45.] Rosenberg, M.B. 2015. *Nonviolent communication: a language of life.* 3rd edn. Puddledancer Press, California, US.

[46.] Kurlansky, M. 2008. *Non-violence: the history of a dangerous idea.* Vintage Books, London UK.

[47.] Braman, L. 2021. Trauma recovery avocado model. https://lindsaybraman.com/trauma-recovery-avocado-model/

[48.] Biddington, T. 2021. Doing dirty theology: how ensoiled humans participate in the flourishing of all earthlings. Feminist Theology 29: 305–317.

[49.] Ball, B.C. 2015. Soil connection: a key to sustainability? In: *'Soil and culture: bringing the arts down to earth'.* Centre for Contemporary Art and the Natural World, Schumacher College, Devon; pp. 102–103.

[50.] McIntosh, A. 2020. *Riders on the storm: the climate crisis and the survival of being.* Birlinn, Edinburgh, UK.

[51.] McIntosh, A. 2014. *Parables of Northern Seed: Anthology from BBC's Thought for the Day.* Wild Goose Publications, Glasgow, UK.

[52.] United Nations Department of Economic and Social Affairs, Sustainable Development https://sdgs.un.org/goals

[53.] Goss, S. 2020. *Garden Mind: an eco-system view of change and a different role for the state.* Compass, UK. https://www.compassonline.org.uk/publications/garden-mind/

[54.] Initiatives of Change International From personal change to global change. Geneva, Switzerland https://www.iofc.org/

A practical and a spiritual journey into soil

[1.] Example Texture Hand Test, Nature for Cities http://natureforcities.snre.umich.edu/wp-content/uploads/2009/nature_city/soils/getting_to_know_your_soil_exp1.pdf USA

[2.] Travis, R. Freedom is a must. Four Thought https://www.bbc.co.uk/sounds/play/m000zsnl BBC Radio 4 Podcast 25 September 2021, UK

[3.] Kumar, S. 2013. *Soil, soul, society: a new trinity for our time.* Leaping Hare Press, Lewes, UK.

[4.] Organics Aeteroa, 2020. 4 guiding principles of organic farming. https://www.oanz.org/new-blog/4-guiding-principles-for-organic-farming New Zealand.

[5.] Grant, B. 2018. Tilling advantages vs. no-till advantages. https://blog.

gardeningknowhow.com/gardening-pros-cons/tilling-advantages-vs-no-till-advantages/

[6.] Klein, N. 2015. How will everything change under climate change? The Guardian, 8 March 2015.

[7.] Join an iListen session https://www.iofc.org/ilisten Initiatives of Change International, Switzerland.

FURTHER READING AND WEBSITES

I Healthy soil

Ashman, M. and Puri, G. 2002. Essential soil science: a clear and concise introduction to soil science. Blackwell, Oxford, UK.
Deals with the basic concepts of soil science in a clear, focused way.
Pavlis, R. 2020. Soil science for gardeners: working with Nature to build soil health. New Society, BC, Canada.
Good practical introduction with details of soil tests and emphasis on soil health and its maintenance.
McLaren, R.G. and Cameron, K.C. 1996. *Soil science: sustainable production and environmental protection (2nd edition).* Oxford University Press.
This is a great text covering many aspects of soils in detail and with clarity. It also has relevance to agriculture and the environment.
Visual Evaluation of Soil Structure (VESS) https://soils.vidacycle.com/soil-tests/vess-visual-evaluation-of-soil-structure/
British Society of Soil Science, a useful resource on UK soils which includes an option to 'find an expert' https://soils.org.uk/
International Union of Soil Sciences (IUSS) The IUSS promotes all branches of soil science, supporting all soil scientists and soil lovers across the world. https://www.iuss.org/
Basic Information on soils from the Nature education Knowledge Project. The material is presented in an interesting way: https://www.nature.com/scitable/knowledge/library/what-are-soils-67647639/
More basic information from the Soil Science Society of America, good on how soils form and how the different types are created: https://www.soils.org/about-soils/basics

II Healthy planet

Blue carbon storage – the soils of coastal wetlands can be significant carbon stores https://oceanservice.noaa.gov/ecosystems/coastal-blue-carbon/

Berry, W. 2009. Bringing it to the table: on farming and food. Counterpoint, California, USA.
Berry, W. 1996. The unsettling of America: culture and agriculture. Sierra Club, California, USA.
Wendell Berry is a farmer who identifies the limitations of most of our current agriculture. The first book of these two focuses on the fallacies of modern farming and on the link between food and the land. The second book establishes the links between agriculture, culture and spirituality with a call to their restoration to conserve communities, fruitful labour and nature. I recommend any book by Wendell Berry.
Ferreira, L.G.B. 2020. *Conservation agriculture.* GlobeEdit, Mauritius.
Gewin, V. 2020. How peat could protect the planet. Nature 578: 204–208.
King, F.H. 1911. *Farmers of forty centuries: permanent agriculture in China, Korea and Japan.* Rodale Press, Pennsylvania, USA.
A fascinating account of basic principles of building soil fertility by soil management using natural processes of composting, crop rotation, green manuring, tillage of several crops per year and irrigation. These are age-old principles.

III Healthy lives

Trellis Scotland a network of Therapeutic Gardens in hospices, care homes, colleges and other areas https://www.trellisscotland.org.uk/content/therapeutic-gardening
LION Land in our names is an initiative to reconnect black communities with land in Britain https://landinournames.community/
Hawken, P. (ed.) 2018. *Drawdown: the most comprehensive plan ever proposed to reverse global warming.* Penguin, UK.
This gives 100 ways to tackle and reverse global warming. It gives numbers to help rank the effectiveness of the various strategies.
Hillel, D. 1992. *Out of the earth. Civilization and the life of the soil.* University of California Press, Los Angeles, USA.
Landa, E.R. and Feller, C. (eds.) 2009. *Soils and culture.* Springer, New York, USA.

Losada, I. 2020. *The joyful environmentalist: how to practise without preaching.* Watkins, London. Lots of ideas here presented in an inspiring style.
Patriotic Millionaires. A group of US millionaires seeking economic and political equality. They campaign against tax cuts and disproportionate advantages to millionaires, billionaires and corporations. https://patrioticmillionaires.org/
Roszak, T., Gomes, M.E. and Kanner, A.D. 1995. *Ecopsychology: restoring the earth, healing the mind.* Sierra Club Books, University of California Press, USA.
New concepts of the relationship between renewal in the environmental movement and mental health are presented.
Thompson, P. B. 1995. *The spirit of the soil: agriculture and environmental ethics.* Routledge, London, UK.
The is a challenging, deep account of the nature of sustainability which attempts to reclaim the spirit of the soil with emphasis on reducing hubris.
Vaze, P. 2009. *The economical environmentalist: my attempt to live the low-carbon life and what it cost.* Earthscan, London, UK.
Useful, practical ideas for everyday low-carbon living. It might put you off long-haul flights.
Wilkinson, R. and Pickett, K. 2009. *The spirit level: why equality is better for everyone.* Penguin, UK.
This gives convincing arguments for reducing inequality which leads to an overall better society and is a strong argument for dealing with poverty.
Meditation resources are readily available on line. See, for example, https://www.youtube.com/c/TheMindfulMovement/videos https://www.youtube.com/c/calm
Meditation as a tool for self-knowledge, based on the studies of Jung, by Daryl Sharp https://frithluton.com/articles/meditation-as-a-tool-for-self-knowledge/

Farmers' and growers' resources

Farmer's practical guidance for using the soil well, (particularly relevant to Scotland). Includes guidance on choice of type of conservation tillage. https://www.sruc.ac.uk/downloads/file/2989/cloy_et_al_-_valuing_your_soils_practical_guidance_for_scottish_farmers

An inspiring farmer's resource hub with emphasis on agroecology and regenerative agriculture https://farmersfootprint.us/resources/?gclid=CjwKCAiAgc-ABhA7EiwAjev-j2AykXtY6SsBrk9KQuWokk2kkOn9hjyxvF7yTVF0Q-H6c_q0C3XbDhoC2OkQAvD_BwE

The Oxford Real Farming Conference is a great resource that claims, with good reason, to be the unofficial gathering of the *real* food and farming movement in the UK. There is a wealth of archival material from all over the world from farmers, growers, activists, policy-makers, researchers and all those who support agroecology, including organic and regenerative agriculture and indigenous systems. https://orfc.org.uk/

Batey, T. 2009. Soil compaction and soil management – a review. Soil Use and Management 25: 335–345.

A highly practical review of the sources, consequences, detection and remediation of compaction.

Ball, B.C. 1986. Cereal production with broadcast seed and reduced tillage: a review of recent experimental and farming experience. Journal of agricultural Engineering Research 35: 71–95.

Seed broadcasting is quicker and can be used in poorer soil conditions than conventional seeding systems, though it needs good control of compaction and weeds.

Brown, G. 2018. *Dirt to soil: one family's journey into Regenerative Agriculture.* Chelsea Green Publishing, London, UK.

Landzettel, M. Regenerative agriculture: Farming with benefits. Profitable farms. Healthy food. Greener planet. World University Service, Germany.

Masters, N. 2019. *For the love of soil: strategies to regenerate our food production systems.* Printable reality, New Zealand.

Salatin, J. 2010. *The sheer ecstasy of being a lunatic farmer.* Polyface, Virginia, USA.

A pioneer of soil-centred farming, Joel Salatin restored a farm with badly degraded soil using agroecological methods. Neighbouring farmers called his ideas those of a lunatic – hence the title – but they worked and his produce is in great demand.

Soils for young people

A great resource for children with soil games and soil experiments: https://www.soils4kids.org/about with accompanying material for their teachers: https://www.soils4teachers.org/soil-basics
Some fun soil experiments for children from the Food and Agriculture Organisation (FAO) https://www.fao.org/3/i7957e/i7957e.pdf
Children's stories of The Magical World of Soil Biodiversity, along with a full report of the State of Knowledge of Soil Biodiversity are downloadable at http://www.fao.org/documents/card/en/c/cb4185en/
Soils in schools: soil topics offering a range of sources tailored to different age groups from uksoils https://uksoils.org/topic/soil-in-schools
Testing soil – simple science for kids https://rainydaymum.co.uk/soil-science-for-kids/

About the author:

Bruce Ball PhD is an internationally-recognised researcher and teacher of soil science. He is a retired Reader in Soil Science, with much experience overseas, and specialises in soil health and greenhouse gas emissions from soil in organic farming and conservation agriculture. Brought up in North-east Scotland, living close to the soil and working on farms from an early age, he has committed much of his life to bringing the wonders of the soil and its importance to the planet to farmers, students, gardeners, schoolchildren and the general public. He is a prolific publisher with 220 technical papers and 27 book chapters and books. His most recent published technical book is Visual Soil Evaluation (CABI Books) – co-authored with Lars Munkholm. Recently he has used spiritual and anthropomorphic ideas along with poetry to further his goal to improve the connection between people and soil. This resulted in the book The Landscape Below (Wild Goose) which paved the way for a succession of invited workshops and lectures. These combined with artworks from recent art classes have allowed him to further develop and express his unique ideas about the centrality of soil to life.

Social media links:

Twitter @BruceCBall
Facebook @BruceCBall
LinkedIn https://www.linkedin.com/in/bruce-ball-aba65639
ResearchGate https://www.researchgate.net/profile/Bruce-Ball

Books by the same author:

Ball, B.C. 2015. The Landscape Below: Soil, Spirituality and Agriculture. Wild Goose, Glasgow, UK. ISBN 9781849523219 (Paperback) ISBN 9781849523240 (Ebook) https://www.ionabooks.com/product/the-landscape-below/

Ball, B.C. and Munkholm, L. R. (eds). 2015. Visual Soil Evaluation: Realising Potential Crop Production with Minimum Environmental Impact. CABI, Wallingford, UK. ISBN 9781780644707 (Hardcover) ISBN 9781780647456 (Paperback) https://www.cabi.org/bookshop/book/9781780644707/

Ball, B.C. 2018. The Spirit of the Borders Railway. Published by the author ISBN 9781910693940 (Paperback); out of print. An eBook version is in press; ISBN: 978-1-7395931-2-4. https://www.scotsman.com/news/telling-midlothian-tales-about-borders-railway-1428545

Soil Health Chart

The colour chart for assessing soil health using the Visual Evaluation of Soil Structure (VESS) is presented opposite. A similar colour chart but without text is shown on page 24. A more complete version of both charts along with a full method description and a scoring sheet for use outdoors are available at:
https://www.sruc.ac.uk/business-services/sac-consulting/agricultural-production/soils/soil-health-testing/

Another description of the technique is available at:
https://soils.vidacycle.com/soil-tests/vess-visual-evaluation-of-soil-structure/

Structure quality	Size and appearance of aggregates	Visible porosity and Roots	Appearance after break-up: various soils	Appearance after break-up: same soil different tillage	Distinguishing feature	Appearance and description of natural or reduced fragment of ~ 1.5 cm diameter
Sq1 Friable Aggregates readily crumble with fingers	Mostly < 6 mm after crumbling	Highly porous Roots throughout the soil		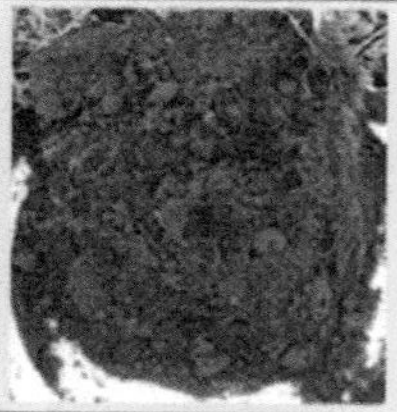	Fine aggregates	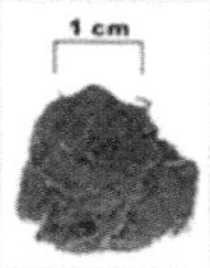 1 cm The action of breaking the block is enough to reveal them. Large aggregates are composed of smaller ones, held by roots.
Sq2 Intact Aggregates easy to break with one hand	A mixture of porous, rounded aggregates from 2mm - 7 cm. No clods present	Most aggregates are porous Roots throughout the soil	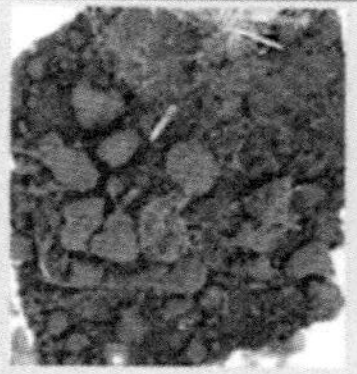		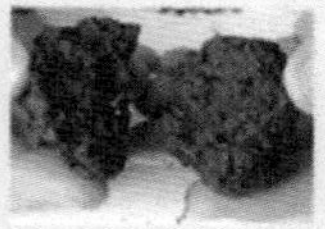 High aggregate porosity	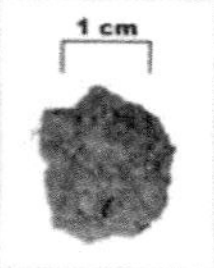 1 cm Aggregates when obtained are rounded, very fragile, crumble very easily and are highly porous.
Sq3 Firm Most aggregates break with one hand	A mixture of porous aggregates from 2mm -10 cm; less than 30% are <1 cm. Some angular, non-porous aggregates (clods) may be present	Macropores and cracks present. Porosity and roots both within aggregates.		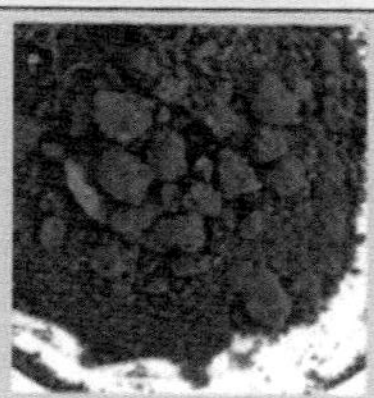	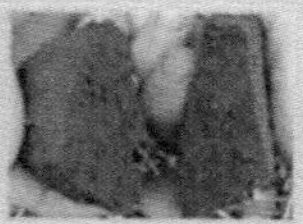 Low aggregate porosity	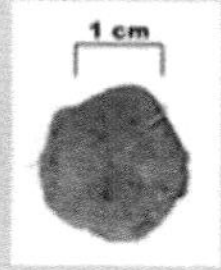 1 cm Aggregate fragments are fairly easy to obtain. They have few visible pores and are rounded. Roots usually grow through the aggregates.
Sq4 Compact Requires considerable effort to break aggregates with one hand	Mostly large > 10 cm and sub-angular non-porous; horizontal/platy also possible; less than 30% are <7 cm	Few macropores and cracks All roots are clustered in macropores and around aggregates			 Distinct macropores	 1 cm Aggregate fragments are easy to obtain when soil is wet, in cube shapes which are very sharp-edged and show cracks internally.
Sq5 Very compact Difficult to break up	Mostly large > 10 cm, very few < 7 cm, angular and non-porous	Very low porosity. Macropores may be present. May contain anaerobic zones. Few roots, if any, and restricted to cracks	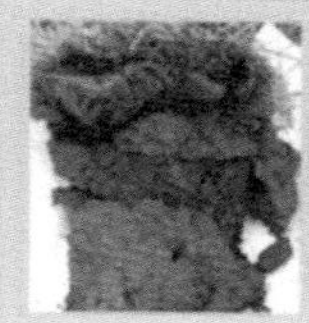		 Grey-blue colour	 1 cm Aggregate fragments are easy to obtain when soil is wet, although considerable force may be needed. No pores or cracks are visible usually.

Printed in Great Britain
by Amazon